The UK Mathematics Trust

Ten Years of Mathematical Challenges

1997 – 2006

This book contains all the Challenge Papers set and operated by the UKMT from 1st January 1997 to 31st August 2006. It contains all the question papers, and solutions.

Published by the United Kingdom Mathematics Trust.
School of Mathematics, The University of Leeds, Leeds LS2 9JT
Telephone: 0113 343 2339
Website: http://www.ukmt.org.uk

Cover design: – The backdrop is a Penrose tiling whose complexity
reflects the activities of the UKMT.

Printed by Cromwell Press Trowbridge Wiltshire

ISBN 1-906001-00-6 (978-1-906001-00-1 from January 2007)

Foreword

This book of UKMT Challenge papers is being published at the time of its tenth anniversary. UKMT was established in the autumn of 1996 and since then has produced and processed ten Junior Challenges, ten Intermediate Challenges but only nine Senior Challenges. In 1996, the National Mathematics Contest was handled by the Mathematical Association.

The book contains all of the 29 challenges and their solutions. In addition, there are photocopiable answer grids which may be of some use. It is not possible to give credit to the considerable team involved in the operation of the Challenge, most are volunteers and very enthusiastic. The growth of the Challenges over the ten years is a tribute to all who gave their time and energy.

The book is presented in a very conventional fashion. The ten JMC papers are followed by the ten IMC papers and then the nine SMC papers. Solutions follow these in an identical fashion. One feature of the solutions is that immediately following the year, there is a set of 25 letters, e.g.

*C B A D E * B E D E C * B E C D A * B B A C A * D B D C E*

These represent the answers. The answers have been included in this fashion for the convenience of the user and also close to the solutions which should encourage these to be studied.

Additonally, there are answer grids at the back of the book which users may find of use.

Contents

Foreword   (i)

Section 1

Question papers

Junior Challenge 1997

1. Four lamp posts are in a straight line. The distance from each post to the next is 25m. What is the distance from the first post to the last?

   A 25m   B 50m   C 75m   D 100m   E 425m

2. On holiday last year Phil Atterlist bought ten postcards for 10p each and ten second class stamps at 19p each. How much change did Phil get from £10?

   A 10p   B £7.10   C £8   D £8.10   E £9.00

3. Which of the following bar charts could represent the data from the pie chart on the right?

   A   B   C   D   E

4. Which of the following expressions gives the largest number?

   A $1 \times 9 + 9 \times 7$ B $1 + 9 + 9 + 7$ C $1 \times 9 + 9 + 7$ D $1 + 9 \times 9 + 7$ E $1 + 9 + 9 \times 7$

5. Kylie the clumsy koala is all fingers and thumbs. Like all koala bears, Kylie has two thumbs and three fingers on each front paw, and one thumb and four fingers on each rear paw. How many thumbs do Kylie and her nine brothers have between them?

   A 10   B 20   C 30   D 40   E 60

6. WHICH LETTER DOES NOT OCCUR MORE THAN ONCE IN THIS QUESTION – INCLUDING THE FIVE OPTIONS?

   A   B   C   D   E

7. Which of these numbers is not a multiple of 3?

   A 12   B 234   C 3456   D 45678   E 567890

8. I have two "Spinners": one is a square, and the other is a regular pentagon. Both spinners are spun at the same time and the two scores obtained are added together. How many possible totals are there?

   A 5   B 6   C 7   D 8   E 9

9. What is the value of $\dfrac{4}{1 - \frac{3}{4}}$?

   A $\dfrac{1}{16}$ B $\dfrac{1}{4}$ C 1   D 4   E 16

10. Each day throughout July 1995 I picked 300g of raspberries from my garden. What was me total weight of the raspberries I picked that month?

    A 10g   B 9kg   C 9.3kg   D 10kg   E 9300kg

11. Each face of a cube is to be painted. Six different colours of paint are available. What is the smallest number of colours one must use if "adjacent" faces (those having an edge in common) never have the same colour?

    A 2   B 3   C 4   D 5   E 6

12. A ball is dropped onto a hard surface. Each time it bounces, it rebounds to exactly one third of the height from which it fell. After the second bounce the ball rises to a height of 9cm. From what height was it originally dropped?

    A 1cm   B 3cm   C 9cm   D 27cm   E 81cm

13. Each of the nine small squares in the diagram are to be filled so that each row and each column contains one 1, one 2 and one 3 in some order. What must $M + N$ be?

    A 2   B 3   C 4   D 5   E 6

14. Which fraction is the biggest?

    A $\dfrac{1+2}{2+3}$ B $\dfrac{2+4}{2+3}$ C $\dfrac{1+2}{4+6}$ D $\dfrac{1+4}{1+3}$ E $\dfrac{3+4}{2+4}$

15. Donna is making a coloured tower as shown. She has thirty six small cubes, with equal numbers of red (R), blue (B) and yellow (Y). Each row is of one colour, and no two rows which are next to each other are the same colour. The top three rows are coloured as indicated. What colour must the bottom row be?

    A red   B blue   C yellow

        D can't be done   E can't be sure

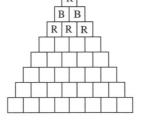

16. Humpty Dumpty sat on a wall, admiring his new digital watch which displayed hours and minutes only. He noticed that it was |5:2| when Jack and Jill set off up the hill, but that when they later came tumbling down again his watch showed only |0:5|. At that point Humpty realised that he'd had his watch on upside down all the time! How long did Jack and Jill take to go up the hill and down again?

    A 40min   B 2hr 10min   C 2hr 20min   D 3hr 10min   E 4hr 30min

17. How big is angle x?

    A 76°   B 104°   C 113°   D 114°   E 150°

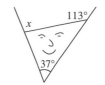

18. A right-angled triangle has the dimensions as shown. What is the area (in cm^2) of the shaded region?

    A 3   B 6   C 9   D 12   E 24

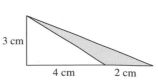

19. A newspaper has thirty six pages. Which other pages are on the same sheet as page 10?

    A 9, 11, 12   B 11, 12, 13   C 9, 27, 28   D 9, 29, 30   E 11, 26, 27

20. A four-digit number was written on a piece of paper. The last two digits were then blotted out (as shown). If the complete number is exactly divisible by three, by four, and by five, what is the sum of the two missing digits?

    8 6 ▯ ▯

    A 4   B 6   C 7   D 9   E 14

21. Tickets for a school play cost £3 for adults and £1 for children. The total amount collected from ticket sales was £1320. The play was staged in a hall seating 600, but the hall was not completely full. What was the smallest possible number of adults at the play?

    A 358   B 359   C 360   D 361   E 362

22. The Grand Old Duke of York, he had ten thousand men, he marched them up to the top of the hill, ... By 2pm they were one third of the way up. By 4pm they were three quarters of the way up. When did they set out?

    A 12 noon   B 12.24pm   C 1.12pm   D 1.36pm   E 1.48pm

23. "My car uses just 8 litres per 100km", boasted Jim. "Mine does 540km on a full 45 litre tank", said Kim. "Mine does 13km per litre", said Lim. Write J (Jim), K (Kim), and L (Lim) in order to represent the three cars – with the most economical car first and the least economical last.

    A KJL   B LKJ   C JKL   D LJK   E KLJ

24. All except four of the nine numbers from 11 to 19 can be put in a single sequence "16, 18, 15, 12, 14" where each successive pair (such as 12 and 14, or 18 and 15) has highest common factor greater than 1. If you make the longest possible sequence like this using as many as possible of the nine numbers from 111 to 119, how many numbers will be left out?

    A 0   B 1   C 2   D 3   E 4

25. Seven towns P, Q, R, S, T, U, V lie (in that order) along a road. The table on the right is meant to give all the distances between pairs of towns (in km): for example, the distance from P to S is 23km. Unfortunately, fifteen of the distances are missing. How many of the missing distances can be calculated from the given information?

P						
?	Q					
?	?	R				
23	?	?	S			
?	30	?	?	T		
58	?	40	?	?	U	
?	68	?	53	?	?	V

    A 0   B 1   C 6   D 12   E 15

Junior Challenge 1998

1. What is the remainder when 2 400 040 002 is divided by 5?

   A 0   B 1   C 2   D 3   E 4

2. An oak was planted to mark the birth of Oliver Albert King. He died in 1911 aged 62. How old is the tree in 1998?

   A 87   B 129   C 147   D 149   E 159

3. $2 \times 17 + 3 \times 17 + 5 \times 17$ equals

   A 160   B 170   C 868   D 10778   E 14960

4. Clearing up after the party I found two pop bottles which were full, two which were one third full, two which were half full, two which were one third empty, two which were half empty, and two which were completely empty. How many bottles did I find altogether?

   A 4   B 6   C 8   D 10   E 12

5. My train was scheduled to leave at 17.42 and to arrive at 18.17. However, it started four minutes late, and the journey took 43 minutes. At what time did 1 arrive?

   A 18.21   B 18.23   C 18.25   D 18.27   E 18.29

6. The network on the right illustrates the relative ages of five children *Uo*, *Ko*, *Jo*, *Mo*, and *Co*. The arrow from *U* to *K* means that *Uo* is *older* than *Ko*. Which is the correct order of ages – *youngest* first?

   A *JUCMK*   B *KCMUJ*   C *JUMCK*   D *KCUMJ*   E *UMCJK*

7. The Mystery Prize at the Bank of England Christmas Party was a pile of crisp new £5 notes, numbered from 659384 up to 659500. What was the value of the prize?

   A £116   B £117   C £580   D £585   E £1420

8. If I add up all the different prime factors of 1998, what answer would I get?

   A 42   B 43   C 48   D 116   E 1001

9. $\triangle + \bullet = *, \triangle = \bullet + \square, \triangle + \triangle + \bullet = * + \square + \square$. Then $\triangle$ equals

   A $* + *$ B $\bullet$ C $\square + \square$ D $*$ E $\square$

10. The digits 0, 1, 2, . . . , 9 are equally spaced around a circle. In the following subtractions each digit is to be replaced by the digit exactly opposite it on the circle.
    Which subtraction then gives the smallest answer?

    A 20 − 19   B 30 − 29   C 40 − 39   D 50 − 49   E 60 − 59

11. Which is the smallest of these fractions?

A $\dfrac{5}{8}$ B $\dfrac{6}{13}$ C $\dfrac{7}{12}$ D $\dfrac{9}{17}$ E $\dfrac{10}{19}$

12. Along which line should an upright mirror be placed so
     that the part of the square on one side of the mirror and
     its reflection form an octagon?

A   B   C   D   E

13. For how many three-digit numbers does the sum of the digits equal 25?

A 2   B 4   C 6   D 8   E 10

14. How much smaller is the area of a 60cm by 40cm rectangle than that of a square with the
     same perimeter?

A 0 cm²   B 10 cm²   C 20 cm²   D 40 cm²   E 100 cm²

15. At the first ever *World Worm-Charming Championship*, held at Wollaston, Cheshire in
     July 1980, Tom Shufflebottom charmed a record 510 worms out of his 3m × 3m patch of
     ground in 30 minutes. If the worms, of average length 20cm, stopped wriggling and were
     laid out end to end round the edge of his patch, approximately how many times round
     would they stretch?

A $8\frac{1}{2}$ B 9   C 20   D 30   E 510

16. Five pings and five pongs are worth the same as two pongs and eleven pings. How many
     pings is a pong worth?

A $\frac{1}{2}$ B 2   C $2\frac{1}{2}$ D 9   E can't be sure

17. Four crosses are to be placed in this 4 by 4 grid so that no two
     crosses go in the same row or column, or in any of the ten
     'diagonals'. The position of the first cross is given. Where must
     the cross go in the third column?

A   B   C   D   E can't be sure

18. The three angles of a triangle are $(x + 10)°$, $(2x − 40)°$, $(3x − 90)°$. Which statement
     about the triangles is correct? 'The triangle is . . .

A right-angled isosceles   B right-angled, but not isosceles   C equilateral

D obtuse-angled and isosceles   E none of A-D

19. What fraction of the large rectangle is shaded?

A $\dfrac{11}{16}$ B $\dfrac{9}{16}$ C $\dfrac{5}{8}$ D $\dfrac{3}{4}$ E $\dfrac{2}{3}$

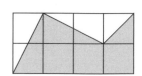

20. Five children *Z, A, B, C, D* are playing a game using a set of ten cards numbered from 1 to 10. They are each dealt two cards with the following totals: $Z = 4, A = 11, B = 12,$ $C = 13, D = 15$. Who has the card number 9?

    A   B   C   D   E can't be sure

21. In a code the vowels A-U in alphabetical order are replaced by the numbers 1-5, while the consonants B-Z in alphabetical order are replaced by the numbers 1-21. Thus '1 1 1 2' could stand for either 'ABAE' or 'BABE'. If the five words below are encoded, and the code numbers for the letters in each word are added up, which word has the largest total?

    A MATHS   B EQUALS   C ALGEBRA   D PLUS   E GEOMETRY

22. Teams from two schools contest a swimming match. Each school enters two swimmers for each event, with 5 points awarded for first place, 3 points for second place, 2 points for third place, and 1 point for fourth place. After six events no swimmer has been disqualified and the leading school's score is the reverse of the other school's score.

    What is the difference between their two scores at this stage?

    A 12   B 18   C 27   D 36   E can't be sure

23. A square is cut into three pieces as shown. Which of the following shapes cannot be made? (You must use all three pieces for each shape.)

    A quadrilateral   B pentagon   C hexagon   D heptagon   E octagon

24. A 5 by 5 by 5 cube is made by gluing 1 by 1 by 1 cubes together. Some of these small cubes are then removed by 'drilling' right through the large cube as shown. How many of the small cubes remain?

    A 50   B 52   C 60   D 68   E 72

25. Sixty 20p coins are lined up side by side. Every second 20p coin is then replaced by a 10p coin. Then every third coin in the resulting row is replaced by a 5p coin. Finally every fourth coin in the row is replaced by a 2p coin. What is the final value of the line?

    A £3.30   B £5.80   C £6.05   D £6.60   E £7.55

Junior Challenge 1999

1. What is two and thirty-four hundredths when written as a decimal?

   A 0.234   B 2.034   C 2.34   D 234.00   E 23400

2. Roughly how much is 200ml?

   A a thimbleful   B a spoonful   C a cupful   D a saucepanful   E a bucketful

3. A wall clock (with hour marks, but no numbers) shows the time as half past ten. If the clock is seen reflected in a vertical mirror, what time would it appear to show?

   A half past one   B 4 o'clock   C 2:30
   D eight hundred hours   E just gone 7 minutes past six

4. What is the remainder when 7 000 010 is divided by 7?

   A 1   B 2   C 3   D 4   E 5

5. For £2, a stamp machine gives a mixture of 20p and 26p stamps worth a total of £2.02. How many 20p stamps are included?

   A 1   B 3   C 5   D 8   E 10

6. What is the value of 19 + 99 + 19 × 99?

   A 236   B 1999   C 11701   D 13563   E none of these

7. Mary has three brothers and four sisters. If they, and Mary, all buy each other an Easter egg, how many eggs will be bought?

   A 14   B 28   C 42   D 56   E 64

8. I owe fifty-five people £55 each. In my piggy bank I have fifty £50 notes and five £5 notes. Is this enough to pay all my debts?

   A Yes, exactly right   B Yes, with a few pounds to spare   C Yes, with lots left over
   D No, a few pounds too little   E No, far too little

9. A "double-decker" sandwich has three slices of bread and two layers of filling (bread/filling/bread/filling/bread). Each slice of bread has to be buttered on each side that is in contact with the filling. I make as many of these sandwiches as possible from a sliced loaf which has 22 usable slices, excluding the crusts which are not used. How many sides of bread do I have to butter?

   A 21   B 22   C 28   D 32   E 42

10. On a journey a certain weight of luggage is carried free, but there is a charge of £10 per kilogram for any additional luggage above this weight. Laa-laa's luggage, which weighs a total of 50kg, is overweight and she is charged £150. If Po's luggage weighs a total of 30kg, what will she have to pay?

    A £0   B £30   C £50   D £90   E £100

11. What is the sum of all the prime numbers which are less than 25?

    A 95   B 98   C 100   D 109   E 115

12. How many different routes are there from S to T which do not go through either of the points U and V more than once?

A 3   B 6   C 8   D 12   E 18

13. In the diagram $\angle RPM = 20°$ and $\angle QMP = 70°$. What is $\angle PRS$?

A 90°   B 110°   C 120°

D 130°   E 140°

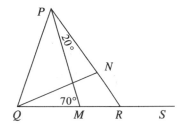

14. A bottle contains 750ml of mineral water. Rachel drinks 50% more than Ross, and these two friends finish the bottle between them. How much does Rachel drink?

A 250 ml   B 375 ml   C 400ml   D 450 ml   E 500 ml

15. A sheet of graph paper is placed with its x-axis pointing due East and its y-axis pointing due North. A sluggish snail starts at point (0,0) and slowly, but smoothly, slithers 1 unit North, 2 units East, 3 units South, 4 units West, 5 units North, 6 units East, 7 units South, 8 units West, 9 units North and (lastly!) 10 units East. At which point does the snail finally arrive?

A $(-6, 5)$ B $(5, 6)$ C $(6, 5)$ D $(6, -5)$ E $(-4, 5)$

16. I have some strange dice: the faces show the numbers 1 to 6 as usual, except that the odd numbers are negative (i.e. $-1, -3, -5$ in place of 1, 3, 5). If I throw two such dice, which total cannot be achieved?

A 3   B 4   C 5   D 7   E 8

17. The 8-digit number 1234*678 is a multiple of 11. Which digit is represented by * ?

A 1   B 3   C 5   D 7   E 9

18. Using all of the digits from 1 to 9 inclusive, Shahb wrote down a fraction which had four digits in the numerator and five digits in the denominator. He then noticed that the fraction simplified to give exactly one half. Which of the following could have been the numerator of Shahb's fraction?

A 5314   B 6729   C 7341   D 7629   E 8359

19. Three shapes X, Y and Z are shown below. A sheet of A4 paper (297 mm by 210 mm) is folded **once**, and placed flat on a table. Which of these shapes could be made?

X

Y

Z

A Y and Z only   B Z and X only   C X and Y only   D none of them   E all of them

20. Which of the cubes below could have been made by folding the net on the right?

A   B

C   D   E

21. Granny says "I am 84 years old – not counting my Sundays". How old is she really?

A 90   B 91   C 96   D 98   E 99

22. How many times between midday and midnight is the hour hand of a clock at right angles to the minute hand?

A 11   B 12   C 20   D 22   E 24

23. In the game illustrated here, the black counter • has to be moved from its "starting position" to its "target position" (shown here as circle ⊙). The aim is to achieve this in the smallest number of "moves". To make a "move", you have to choose one of the fifteen marked lines as your "mirror" and move the counter • to the position which is the reflection of its present position in that "mirror". What is the smallest number of "moves" required to reach the target position?

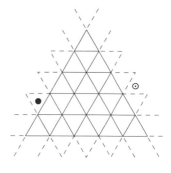

A 2   B 3   C 4   D 5
E Starting from • it is impossible to reach ⊙

24. Boris, Spike and Percival are going to race up the 99 steps that lead from the beach to the car park at the top of the cliff. Boris can run up five steps in the same time as Spike can run up four steps, which is the same time as Percival can run up three steps. It is agreed that Boris starts from the bottom, Spike starts 21 steps up and Percival 38 steps up. If they all start at the same time, in what order will they reach the top?

A SBP   B SPB   C PBS   D PSB   E BSP

25. The two-digit by two-digit multiplication on the right has lots of gaps, but most of them can be filled in by logic (not by guesswork). Which digit must go in position * ?

A 1   B 3   C 5   D 7   E 9

```
        4 –
  ×   –  –
  ─────────
    –  8  –
    8  –  0
  ─────────
  –  –  4  *
  ─────────
```

Junior Challenge 2000

1. What is half of 999?

   A 444½   B 449½   C 454½   D 494½   E 499½

2. Sir Isaac Newton, the English mathematician, physicist and discoverer of the laws of gravity, was born in Woolsthorpe, Lincolnshire in 1642, the same year that Galileo, the Italian scientist, died.

   How many years ago was that?

   A 351   B 358   C 368   D 424   E 442

3. What is the value of *x*?

   A 22   B 28   C 108   D 130   E 208

4. Which of the following has the greatest value?

   A $(1 \times 2) \times (3 \times 4)$ B $(1 \times 2) + (3 \times 4)$ C $(1 \times 2) \times (3 + 4)$

   D $(1 + 2) \times (3 \times 4)$ E $(1 + 2) \times (3 + 4)$

5. Which of the following could be the image of U K M T when seen reflected in a mirror?

   A ∩KWꓕ   B TMKU   C UꓘMT   D ∩ꓘWꓕ   E ꓕWꓘ∩

6. A transport company's vans each carry a maximum load of 12 tonnes. A firm needs to deliver 24 crates each weighing 5 tonnes. How many van loads will be needed to do this?

   A 9   B 10   C 11   D 12   E 13

7. Today, the sun rose at Greenwich at 6:45 am and will set 12 hours and 44 minutes later. At what time will the sun set at Greenwich today?

   A 6:29 pm   B 7:09 pm   C 7:29 pm   D 7:39 pm   E 9:29 pm

8. A single piece of string is threaded through five holes in a piece of card. One side of the card is shown in the diagram on the right. Which of the diagrams below could *not* represent the pattern of the string on the reverse side?

   A   B   C   D   E

9.   Three-quarters of the junior members of a tennis club are boys and the rest are girls. What is the ratio of boys to girls among these members?

     A 3 : 4   B 4 : 3   C 3 : 7   D 4 : 7   E 3 : 1

10. Each Junior Mathematical Challenge answer sheet weighs 6 grams. If 140 000 pupils enter the Challenge this year, what will be the total weight of all their answer sheets?

     A 84 kg   B 840 kg   C 8 400 kg   D 84 000 kg   E 840 000 kg

11. The digits of this year, 2000 A.D., add up to 2. In how many *other* years since 1 A.D. has this happened?

     A 3   B 6   C 8   D 9   E 10

12. Four rectangular paper strips, each measuring 10 cm by 1 cm, are laid flat on a table. Each strip is at right angles to two of the other strips as shown.

     What is the area of the table covered by the strips?

     A 30 cm^2 B 32 cm^2 C 34 cm^2 D 36 cm^2 E 38 cm^2

13. 48% of the pupils at a certain school are girls. 25% of the girls and 50% of the boys at this school travel to school by bus. What percentage of the whole school travel by bus?

     A 37%   B 38%   C 62%   D 73%   E 75%

14. The DISPUTOR is similar to a calculator, but it behaves a little oddly. When you type in a number, the DISPUTOR doubles the number, then reverses the digits of this result, then adds 2 and displays the final result. I type in a whole number between 10 and 99 inclusive. Which of the following could be the final result displayed?

     A 39   B 41   C 42   D 43   E 45

15. Dilly is 7 years younger than Dally. In 4 years time she will be half Dally's age. What is the sum of their ages now?

     A 13   B 15   C 17   D 19   E 21

16. A book has 256 pages with, on average, 33 lines on each page and 9 words on each line. Which of the following is the best approximation to the number of words in the book?

     A 64 000   B 68 000   C 72 000   D 76 000   E 80 000

17. The first and third digits of the five-digit number $d6d41$ are the same. If the number is exactly divisible by 9, what is the sum of its five digits?

     A 18   B 23   C 25   D 27   E 30

18. A circle is added to the grid alongside. What is the largest number of dots that the circle can pass through?

     A 4   B 6   C 8   D 10   E 12

19. The numbers $\frac{1}{2}$, x, y, $\frac{3}{4}$ are in increasing order of size. The differences between successive numbers in this list are all the same. What is the value of y?

    A $\dfrac{3}{8}$ B $\dfrac{2}{3}$ C $\dfrac{7}{12}$ D $\dfrac{5}{6}$ E $\dfrac{5}{8}$

20. Despite his name, Mr. Bean likes to eat lots of fruit. He finds that four apples and two oranges cost £1.54 and that two oranges and four bananas cost £ 1.70. How much would he have to pay if he bought one apple, one orange and one banana?

    A 77p   B 78p   C 79p   D 80p   E 81p

21. Tick's watch runs 2 minutes per hour too slow. Tock's watch runs 1 minute per hour too fast. They set them to the same time at noon on Sunday. The next time they met, one of the watches was one hour ahead of the other. What was the earliest time this could have been?

    A 8am on Monday   B 7:20 pm on Monday   C 4am on Tuesday

             D midnight on Wednesday   E 10 pm on Saturday

22. Four identical blocks of wood are placed touching a table in the positions shown in this side-on view. How high is the table?

    A 84cm   B 87cm   C 90cm   D 93cm   E 96cm

23. A certain number has exactly eight factors including 1 and itself. Two of its factors are 21 and 35. What is the number?

    A 105   B 210   C 420   D 525   E 735

24. The six cards shown display the number 632579. One "turn" consists of exchanging the positions of two adjacent cards so, for instance, after one "turn" the cards could show 632759. Starting from the original 632579, what is the least number of "turns" required so that the cards display a number which is divisible by 4?

    A 2   B 3   C 4   D 5   E 6

25. In a magic square each row, each column and both main diagonals have the same total. What number should replace x in this partially completed magic square?

    A 4   B 9   C 10   D 12

    E more information needed

13		
5		15
x		

Junior Challenge 2001

1. Last Saturday, each half of a hockey match lasted 40 minutes and the half-time interval was a quarter of an hour. The match started at 2:30 pm. At what time did it finish?

    A 3:10 pm   B 3:25 pm   C 3:50 pm   D 3:55 pm   E 4:05 pm

2. The diagram shows 6 small squares made with matchsticks. How many matchsticks must be removed to leave precisely 3 small squares which touch only at corners?

    A 3   B 4   C 5   D 6   E 7

3. The theme music for the famous science-fiction film *2001: A Space Odyssey* is taken from *Also Sprach Zarathustra*, which was written by Richard Strauss in 1896. How many years was that before the film itself was produced in 1968?

    A 72   B 33   C 28   D 105   E 82

4. What is 40% of 50% of £60?

    A £7   B £8   C £12   D £15   E £20

5. A 'Supertape' plays for 6 hours. It rewinds 18 times as quickly as it plays. How many minutes does it take to rewind a Supertape completely?

    A 3   B 18   C 20   D 108   E 180

6. Last year, to help sell his house, Southampton butcher Simon Broadribb offered to give the buyer meat worth £20 every week for one year. It was stated that this could be either 40 burgers, or 96 sausages, or 140 rashers of bacon, or 30 lamb cutlets, or 35 portions of mince. Based on that offer, which is the most expensive?

    A a burger   B a sausage   C a rasher of bacon

         D a lamb cutlet   E a portion of mince

7. A guinea-pig in a large field is tethered to one end of a 10 metre rope. The other end of the rope is attached to a ring which is free to slide along a fixed horizontal rail, 10 metres long, in the middle of the field. Which diagram shows the shape of the part of the field that the guinea-pig can reach?

8. What is the difference between the largest and smallest of the following numbers?

    A 0.89   B 0.9   C 0.17   D 0.72   E 0.73

9. In the diagram, a corner of the shaded star is at the midpoint of each side of the large square. What fraction of the large square is covered by the star?

    A $\frac{1}{5}$ B $\frac{1}{4}$ C $\frac{1}{3}$ D $\frac{3}{8}$ E $\frac{2}{5}$

10. If the digit 4 is replaced by the digit 3 in each of the numbers below, which number is reduced by the largest amount?

   A 45678   B 87654   C 95400   D 74000   E 99949

11. At half time in a netball match, Jokers were leading Jesters by 3 goals to 2. Seven goals were scored in the second half. Which of the following could *not* have been the result of the match?

   A The match was drawn   B Jesters won by 2 goals   C Jesters won by 4 goals
              D Jokers won by 2 goals   E Jokers won by 3 goals

12. The sheet of paper shown on the left is folded along the dotted lines (each fold being either forwards or backwards) to make the leaflet shown on the right. Each of the six 'pages' of the leaflet is printed in a different colour. No matter how it is folded, the leaflet will have two pages visible on the outside. How many different pairs of outside pages can be obtained by folding the sheet of paper in different ways?

   A 4   B 6   C 9   D 12   E 15

13. A newspaper reported last year that marine experts at the Sea Life Centre in Brighton were teaching an octopus to open jam jars to get at food as a way of stopping it becoming bored. Assuming that it can open four jars simultaneously and that each jar takes 30 seconds to open, how many jars can the octopus open per hour?

   A 30   B 120   C 240   D 480   E 960

14. How many of the following nets could be folded to make a cube?

   A 1   B 2   C 3   D 4   E 5

15. It is well known that the Pobble has no toes, and that the three-toed sloth has 12 toes (3 on each of its 4 feet). A synchronised swimming team is made up of 7 Pobbles and 5 three-toed sloths. What is the mean number of toes per team member?

   A 3   B 4   C 5   D 6   E 7

16. My bus fare is 44p. If the driver can give me change, what is the smallest number of coins which must change hands when I pay this fare?

   A 2   B 3   C 4   D 5   E 6

17. Lollipops cost 12p each, but I get 3 for 30p. What is the maximum number of lollipops I can buy if I have £2 to spend?

   A 16   B 17   C 18   D 19   E 20

18. Triangle *PQR* is equilateral. Angle *SPR* = 40°, angle *TQR* = 35°.
     What is the size of the marked angle *SXT*?

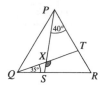

     A 140°   B 135°   C 120°   D 105°   E 75°

19. Given that $\dfrac{1}{12} + \dfrac{1}{24} = \dfrac{1}{x}$, what is the value of *x*?

     A $\dfrac{1}{18}$ B $\dfrac{1}{8}$ C 8   D 18   E 36

20. The numbers from 1 to 9 inclusive are to be placed, one
     number to a square, in the figure shown, so that the total of the
     three numbers in each of the four lines is the same. What
     number should replace * ?

     A 5   B 6   C 7   D 8   E 9

21. What is the value of $2^8 \div 8^2$?

     A $\dfrac{1}{4}$ B $\dfrac{1}{2}$ C 1   D 2   E 4

22. A rectangular piece of card measuring 30 cm by 24 cm is cut into two equal pieces which
     can be reassembled to form another rectangle measuring 18 cm by 40 cm. Which diagram
     shows the original rectangle and the cut?

     A   B   C   D   E

23. Granny tells Dilly that her glove drawer contains 1 left-hand blue glove, 2 left-hand green
     gloves, 3 right-hand blue gloves, and 4 right-hand green gloves, and asks her to bring a pair
     of gloves from the drawer. Unfortunately Dilly cannot tell the difference between left-
     hand and right-hand gloves, but, thankfully, can identify blue and green. What is the
     smallest number of gloves that Dilly should bring, in order to be sure that these include a
     matching pair?

     A 2   B 4   C 6   D 8   E 10

24. To celebrate this year, 2001, a square pavement is made using equal sized square tiles,
     coloured either red or blue. In the pattern all the tiles are red apart from those along the
     two main diagonals, which are made using a total of 2001 blue tiles. How many red tiles
     are needed?

     A 1 000 000   B 996 000   C 250 000   D 1 002 001   E 4 002 000

25. The diagram shows four overlapping squares which have sides 5,
     7, 9 and 11. What is the difference between the total area shaded
     grey and the total area shaded black?

     A 25   B 36   C 49   D 64
     E more information needed

Junior Challenge 2002

1. What is 2002×5 ?

   A 10 010   B 100 010   C 100 100   D 10 100   E 100 001

2. Which of the following statements is false?

   A $3 + 5 \times 4 = 23$ B $20 - 5 \times 4 = 0$ C $12 - 5 \times 2 = 2$

   D $3 + 6 \times 4 = 36$ E $5 \times 3 - 2 = 13$

3. Which of the following has the biggest value?

   A 1/2 of 24   B 1/3 of 36   C 1/4 of 60   D 1/5 of 50   E 1/6 of 84

4. The diagram shows a square drawn inside an equilateral triangle. What is the size of angle JMC?

   A 90°   B 60°   C 45°   D 30°   E 15°

5. How many of the following numbers are multiples of 5?

   A 1   B 2   C 3   D 4   E 5

6. What is the value of $101 + 2002 + 30003 + 400004 + 5000005$?

   A 5432115   B 15012345   C 5432345   D 5234325   E 54321012345

7. The sum of seven, single-digit positive whole numbers is 17. Six of these numbers are equal, so what is the other number?

   A 1   B 3   C 5   D 7   E 9

8. The diagram shows two circles enclosed in a rectangle measuring 9 cm × 5 cm. What is the distance between the centres of the circles?

   A 2 cm   B 2.5 cm   C 3 cm   D 3.5 cm   E 4 cm

9. Lisa's bucket does not have a hole in it and weighs 21 kg when full of water. After she pours out half the water from the bucket, it weighs 12 kg. What is the weight of the empty bucket?

   A 1 kg   B 2 kg   C 3 kg   D 4 kg   E 5 kg

10. On the island of Erewhon, all numbers are written with the digits in reverse order. For example, twelve is written 21. Su Erasmus, an inhabitant of Erewhon, was shown the subtraction $729 - 45$. If no mistake was made, what answer did Su write down?

    A 684   B 486   C 279   D 873   E 378

11. The Pythagoras School of Music has 100 students. Of these, 60 are in the band and 20 are in the orchestra. Given that 12 students are in both the band and the orchestra, how many are in neither the band nor the orchestra?

    A 8   B 20   C 24   D 28   E 32

12. My rabbit Nibbles lives in a movable pen and helps to keep the grass short. The pen is rectangular and measures 3 m by 2 m, as shown in the diagram, where the arrow indicates North. On successive days, the pen is moved 1 m East, 2 m South, 1 m West and 2 m North. What is the total area, in square metres, of the region of grass which Nibbles can nibble?

A 6   B 12   C 15   D 18   E 24

13. The number 2002 is a *palindrome*, since it reads the same forwards and backwards. For how many other years this century will the number of the year be a palindrome?

A   none   B 1   C 9   D 81   E 90

14. The diagram shows four empty glasses with their bases at the bottom. One move consists of turning exactly three of the four glasses upside-down. What is the smallest number of moves needed before all of the glasses have their bases at the top?

A 3   B 4   C 7   D 11   E 13

15. In which of the following lists are the terms *not* increasing?

A $\frac{1}{5}, 0.25, \frac{3}{10}, 0.5$ B $\frac{3}{5}, 0.7, \frac{4}{5}, 1.5$ C $\frac{2}{5}, 0.5, \frac{7}{10}, 0.9$

D $\frac{3}{5}, 0.5, \frac{4}{5}, 0.9$ E $\frac{2}{5}, 1.5, \frac{10}{5}, 2.3$

16. The diagram shows a poster which Beatrix has (this way up!) on her wall. When Beatrix was standing on her head, looking in a mirror on the opposite wall at the poster on the wall behind her, how many letters could still be read in the normal way?

A 2   B 3   C 4   D 5   E 7

17. 5p, 2p and 1p coins (or a mixture of any or all of these) are used to make a total of 11p. In how many different ways can this be done?

A   13   B 11   C 9   D 6   E 3

18. A square piece of paper measuring 16 × 16 is folded in half twice. Then pieces are removed by cutting through all the resulting layers, leaving the shape shown. When the paper is unfolded, how many square holes are in it?

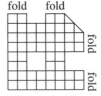

A 1   B 2   C 6   D 7   E 9

19. The number of diagonals of a regular polygon equals twice the number of sides. How many sides has the polygon?

A 4   B 5   C 6   D 7   E 8

20. Sally has 72 small wooden cubes, each measuring 1 cm × 1 cm × 1 cm. She arranges them all so that they form a cuboid. Given that the perimeter of the base of the cuboid is 16 cm, what is its height?

A 4 cm   B 6 cm   C 8 cm   D 9 cm   E 12 cm

21.

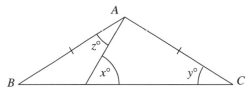

Given that $AB = AC$ and $z < 90$, which of the following expressions must equal z?

A $x - y$ B $x + y$ C $x + y - 180$ D $180 + x - y$ E $180 - x + y$

22. When 26 is divided by a positive integer N, the remainder is 2. What is the sum of all the possible values of N?

A 21   B 33   C 45   D 57   E 70

23. The diagram shows a circle with circumference 1 being rolled around an equilateral triangle with sides of length 1. How many complete turns does the circle make as it rolls once around the triangle without slipping?

A 3   B $3\frac{1}{2}$ C 4   D 5   E $5\frac{1}{2}$

24. In the multiplication

$$\begin{array}{r} AB \\ \times\,C \\ \hline DE \end{array}$$

each letter represents a different digit and only the digits 1, 2, 3, 4, 5 are used. Which of the letters represents 2 ?

A   B   C   D   E

25. Gill sat the JMC last year, when the scoring system used was the same as this year's system. She answered all the questions she did correctly. The first question took her 1 second, question 2 took her 2 seconds, question 3 took her 4 seconds and so on, the time doubling for each question. What was Gill's score?

A 30   B 55   C 60   D 125   E 135

Junior Challenge 2003

1. What is half of 199?

   A 94½   B 95   C 95½   D 99   E 99½

2. A comb for horses has 100 teeth, each 1 mm wide. The gaps
   between the teeth are also 1 mm wide. How long is the comb?

   A 9.9 cm   B 10 cm   C 19 cm   D 19.9 cm   E 20 cm

3. Our Geography teacher, Mr Ridge, takes 7 minutes to mark each pupil's test.
   He has a class of 32. How many minutes marking will he save if 9 of the class are absent?

   A 63   B 161   C 224   D 246   E 287

4. Sam has six plain-coloured plates hanging on her lounge wall, in the
   formation shown. What is the smallest number of plates that need to
   be moved to turn this formation upside down?

   A 1   B 2   C 3   D 4   E 5

5. Yesterday, the reading on Granny's electricity meter was 098657. She was shocked to
   realise that all six of these digits are different. How many more units of electricity will she
   use before the next time all the digits are different?

   A 1   B 4   C 14   D 55   E 3688

6. Referring to the rectangles below, the largest is red and the smallest is blue. Orange is the
   same size as yellow and not next to blue. Which is orange?

   A   B   C   D   E

7. In California, a bottle of orange juice costs $3, but when you return the bottle you get $2
   back. What is the largest number of bottles of juice you can buy if you start with $10?

   A 3   B 6   C 8   D 9   E 10

8. I saw the following numbers on cars on the way to school. Each number, with one
   exception, has the same remainder when divided by 9. Which is the exception?

   A 113   B 257   C 554   D 725   E 861

9. The mean age of the four members of 'All Sinners' boy band is 19. What is the mean age
   when an extra member who is 24 years old joins them?

   A 19   B 20   C 21   D 22   E 24

10. Correct to one decimal place, what is the square root of 18?

    A 2.6   B 3.0   C 3.6   D 4.2   E 9.0

11. Nicolas wrote a Christmas card for each of his three sisters – Carol, Holly and Ivy – and put each card into a separate envelope. In how many different ways can he send a card to each sister so that none of them receives the correct card?

A 1   B 2   C 3   D 4   E 5

12. What is the size of the angle marked x?

A 42°   B 67°   C 69°

D 71°   E 111°

Not to scale

113°   109°

13. This is a prime year, since 2003 is a prime number. In the next ten years there is just one prime year. Which is it?

A 2005   B 2007   C 2009   D 2011   E 2013

14. In the sequence which begins 2, 3, 5, 10, … each number after the second is the sum of all the previous numbers in the sequence. What is the 10th number in the sequence?

A 47   B 170   C 640   D 1280   E 2560

15. It was reported recently that, in an average lifetime of 70 years, each human is likely to swallow about 8 spiders while sleeping. Supposing that the population of the UK is around 60 million, what is the best estimate of the number of unfortunate spiders consumed in this way in the UK each year?

A 50 000   B 600 000   C 7 000 000   D 80 000 000   E 900 000 000

16.   A 6 B C   In this multiplication each letter stands for a different digit. Which
        ×   7   letter stands for 3 ?
     ‾‾‾‾‾‾‾‾‾‾
      D 9 E 9 8   A   B   C   D   E

17. A rectangle is formed by doubling both the length and the width of the rectangle shown in the diagram. What is the area, in cm^2, of this new rectangle?

$(a + 3)$ cm

2 cm

A $2a + 10$ B $4a + 12$ C $4a + 20$ D $8a + 6$ E $8a + 24$

18. The UKMT logo shows a single strip of paper with 'UKMT' in the positions X, Y and Z. Which of these are written on the same side of the paper?

A X and Y B Y and Z C X and Z

D X, Y and Z E none of them

Z UKMT   UKMT Y

X

UKMT

19. When the diagram below is complete, the number in the middle of each group of 3 adjoining cells is the mean of its two neighbours. What number goes in the right-hand end cell?

| 8 | | 20 | |

A 12   B 14   C 16   D 24   E 28

20. The diagram shows a rectangular wire grid which forms twelve small squares. The length of the grid is a. What is the total length of wire required to make the grid?

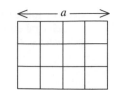

A $9a$ B $\dfrac{17a}{2}$ C $\dfrac{31a}{4}$ D $7a$ E $\dfrac{13a}{2}$

21. The board for the game *Rorrim* is shown. In the game, a counter has to be moved from the starting square, **S**, to the target square, **T**, in the smallest possible number of moves. To make a move, one of the lines of the board is chosen as a mirror and the counter is moved to the square which is the reflection of its present square in that mirror. What is the smallest number of moves required to reach square **T** from square **S** ?

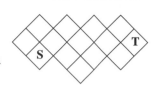

A 3   B 4   C 5   D 6   E 7

22. Two builders, Bob and Geri, buy bricks at the same price. Bob sells 10 for £6 and Geri sells 12 for £7. Supposing they sell equal numbers of bricks, what number has each sold when Bob has gained £4 more than Geri?

A 42   B 60   C 72   D 120   E 240

23. In the diagram alongside, $AB = AC$ and $AD = CD$. How many of the following statements are true for the angles marked?

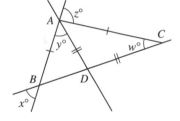

   $w = x$ $x + y + z = 180$ $z = 2x$

A all of them   B two   C one
        D none of them   E it depends on x

24. Gill has recently moved to a new house, which has a three-digit number. The sum of this number and its three individual digits is 429. What is the *product* of the three digits which make up the house number?

A 20   B 28   C 30   D 36   E 48

25. A cardboard cube is cut along its edges by a cut following the line shown in the diagram.

The cube is then opened out and placed flat on a table.

Which of the following could be the resulting shape?

 A   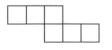   B   C

        D   E

Junior Challenge 2004

1. How many letters of the word **MATHEMATICS** do not have any lines of symmetry?

   A 0   B 1   C 2   D 3   E 4

2. Which of the following numbers is exactly divisible by 7?

   A 104   B 106   C 108   D 110   E 112

3. The year 2004 has the units digit equal to twice the thousands digit. How many years will it be before this next happens?

   A 10   B 36   C 220   D 1002   E 2004

4. A ladybird has landed at point P on Sam's bow-tie. If it travels only along the edges of the bow-tie, but cannot travel along any edge more than once, how many different ways are there for it to get from P to Q?

   A 1   B 2   C 3   D 4   E 5

5. The word 'thirty' contains 6 letters and $6 = 30 \div 5$. Similarly, the word 'forty' contains 5 letters and $5 = 40 \div 8$. Which of the following is not a multiple of the number of letters it contains?

   A six   B twelve   C eighteen   D seventy   E ninety

6. Which of these fractions is nearest to 1?

   A $\dfrac{12}{23}$ B $\dfrac{23}{34}$ C $\dfrac{34}{45}$ D $\dfrac{45}{56}$ E $\dfrac{56}{67}$

7. In music, a demisemiquaver is half of half of half a crotchet, and there are four crotchets in a semibreve. How many demisemiquavers are there in a semibreve?

   A 8   B 16   C 32   D 64   E 128

8. A solid square-based pyramid has all of its corners cut off, as shown. How many edges does the resulting shape have?

   A 8   B 13   C 15   D 20   E 24

9. The Bean family are very particular about beans. At every meal all Beans eat some beans. Pa Bean always eats more beans than Ma Bean but never eats more than half the beans. Ma Bean always eats the same number of beans as both children together and the two children always eat the same number of beans as each other. At their last meal they ate 23 beans altogether. How many beans did Pa Bean eat?

   A 7   B 9   C 11   D 13   E 15

10. When Harry bought his train ticket he received £2.50 in change. He noticed that for each coin in his change there was exactly one other coin of the same value. What was the coin of smallest value in Harry's change?

   A 2p   B 5p   C 10p   D 20p   E 50p

11. The diagram shows a rod with five equally spaced points *A*, *B*, *C*, *D* and *E* marked on it.

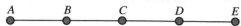

A   B   C   D   E

The rod is rotated three times through 180 degrees, first about *A*, then about *B* and finally about *E*. Which point finishes in the same position as it was at the start?

A *A*   B *B*   C *C*   D *D*   E *E*

12. The White Rabbit has an appointment to see the Red Queen at 4pm every day apart from weekends. On Monday, he arrives 16 minutes late. Each day after that he hurries more and more and so manages to halve the amount of time that he arrives late each day. On what day of the week does he arrive just 15 seconds late?

A Monday   B Tuesday   C Wednesday   D Thursday   E Friday

13. In the triangle *PQR*, the angle *QPR* = 40° and the internal bisectors of the angles at *Q* and *R* meet at *S*, as shown. What is the size of angle *QSR*?

A 110°   B 120°   C 130°   D 135°   E 140°

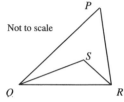

Not to scale

14. The Kings of Clubs, Diamonds, Hearts and Spades, and their respective Queens, are having an arm wrestling competition. Everyone must wrestle everyone else, except that no King will wrestle his own Queen. How many wrestling bouts are there?

A   12   B   16   C   24   D   28   E   64

15. Granny spends one third of her weekly pension on Thursday night, and one quarter of what remains on Friday. What fraction of the original amount is left for her big night out on Saturday?

A $\dfrac{1}{12}$ B $\dfrac{2}{7}$ C $\dfrac{5}{12}$ D $\dfrac{1}{2}$ E $\dfrac{11}{12}$

16. A robot, which is initially facing North, is programmed to travel 5m then turn through 10°, travel 5m then turn through 20°, travel 5m then turn through 30°, and so on. Each move consists of moving 5m in a straight line and then turning clockwise through an angle which increases by 10° at each move.

How far has it travelled by the time it is first facing due East at the end of a move?

A   9 m   B   40 m   C   45 m   D   50 m   E   90 m

17. Exactly one of these statements is correct. Which one?

A $44^2 + 77^2 = 4477$ B $55^2 + 66^2 = 5566$ C $66^2 + 55^2 = 6655$

D $88^2 + 33^2 = 8833$ E $99^2 + 22^2 = 9922$

18. A shape consisting of 2004 small squares is made by continuing the pattern shown in the diagram. The small squares have sides of length 1cm. What is the length, in cm, of the perimeter of the whole shape?

A 4008   B 4010   C 6012   D 6016   E 8016

19. If $a \times b = 2, b \times c = 24, c \times a = 3$ and a, b and c are all positive, what is the value of $a + b + c$?

A 7½   B 10½   C 12   D 16   E 19

20. The figure shows a regular pentagon *PQRST* together with three sides *XP, PR, RU* of a regular hexagon with vertices *PRUVWX*. What is the size of angle *SRU*?

A 48°   B 54°   C 60°   D 63°   E 72°

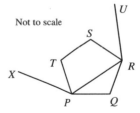

Not to scale

21. Four of these jigsaw pieces fit together to form a rectangle. Which one is not used?

A   B   C   D   E

22. The digits in the product $13 \times 2 - 26$ can be rearranged to give $16 \times 2 = 32$ as well as $31 \times 2 = 62$. In which one of the following can the digits not be rearranged to give another correct product?

A $12 \times 3 = 36$ B $12 \times 7 = 84$ C $26 \times 3 = 78$ D $16 \times 3 = 48$ E $39 \times 2 = 78$

23. In this addition each letter stands for a different digit, with *S* standing for 3. What is the value of $Y \times O$?

A 0   B 2   C 36   D 40   E 42

$$\begin{array}{r} S \ O \\ + \ M \ A \ N \ Y \\ \hline S \ U \ M \ S \end{array}$$

24. Five identical rectangles fit together as shown. What, in cm², is the total area which they cover?

A 270   B 300   C 330   D 360   E 450

15 cm

Not to scale

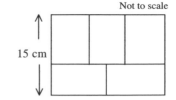

25. In a sequence of positive integers, every term after the first two terms is the sum of the two previous terms in the sequence. If the fifth term is 2004, what is the maximum possible value of the first term?

A 399   B 400   C 663   D 999   E 1001

Junior Challenge 2005

1. The value of $1000 - 100 + 10 - 1$ is:

   A 111   B 900   C 909   D 990   E 999

2. The diagram shows a pattern made from matchsticks stuck to a piece of card. What is the smallest number of matchsticks that need to be added so that the resulting pattern has a line of symmetry?

   A 0   B 1   C 2   D 3   E 4

3. Gollum eats fish on alternate days. How often does he eat fish on a Monday?

   A Twice a day   B Once a week   C Once a fortnight   D Once a month   E Once a year

4. If you looked in a mirror at an accurate clock at 1:30 pm, which of the following would you see?

   A   B   C   D   E

5. Which of the following numbers is *not* the difference between two of the others?

   A 1   B 7   C 6   D 5   E 2

6. Jonny's rat is a slow learner! Every time it goes through this maze, it visits every square at least once. What is the smallest possible number of squares it visits more than once when it goes through the maze?

   A 0   B 1   C 2   D 3   E 4

7. The lightest seeds in the world are probably those of the Creeping Lady's-tresses Orchid, 500 000 of which would weigh 1 gram. How many millions of these seeds weigh 1 kilogram?

   A 2   B 200   C 500   D 5 000   E 1 000 000

8. Peg has six times as much chocolate as Reg. Meg has twice as much chocolate as Reg. Peg has how many times as much chocolate as Meg?

   A Three times as much   B Four times as much   C Eight times as much
               D Ten times as much   E Twelve times as much

9. Beatrix takes a sheet of paper (shown on the far left), folds the sheet in half 4 times and punches a hole all the way through the folded sheet, as shown on the near left. She then unfolds the sheet. How many holes are there now in the unfolded sheet?

   A 4   B 6   C 8   D 12   E 16

10. On Monday last week Dilly started to learn the Tlingit language. Every day she learnt five new words, but when she woke every morning she had forgotten two of the words learnt the day before. When did Dilly first achieve her target of learning fourteen words?

    A Friday   B Monday   C Saturday   D Thursday   E Wednesday

11. Which one of the sectors in the pie chart represents the **mode**?

    A   B   C   D   E

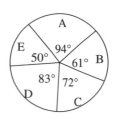

12. Which one of these calculations is **incorrect**?

    A $4 \times 5 + 67 = 45 + 6 \times 7$ B $3 \times 7 + 48 = 37 + 4 \times 8$ C $6 \times 3 + 85 = 63 + 8 \times 5$

    D $2 \times 5 + 69 = 25 + 6 \times 9$ E $9 \times 6 + 73 = 96 + 7 \times 3$

13. The diagram shows two equal squares. What is the value of x?

    not to scale

    A 140   B 145   C 150
          D 155   E 160

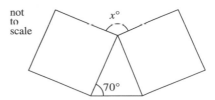

14. If the following fractions are arranged in increasing order of size, which one is in the middle?

    A $\dfrac{1}{2}$ B $\dfrac{2}{3}$ C $\dfrac{3}{5}$ D $\dfrac{4}{7}$ E $\dfrac{5}{9}$

15. There are six different three-digit numbers, each of which contains all the digits 1, 3 and 5. How many of these three-digit numbers are prime?

    A 0   B 1   C 2   D 3   E 4

16. 'Saturn' chocolate bars are packed either in boxes of 5 or boxes of 12. What is the smallest number of full boxes required to pack exactly 2005 'Saturn' bars?

    A 118   B 167   C 168   D 170   E 401

17. The figure shows rectangle *PRSU* and line *QT*, which divides the rectangle into two squares. How many right-angled triangles can be drawn using any three of the points *P, Q, R, S, T, U* as corners?

    A 8   B 9   C 10   D 12   E 14

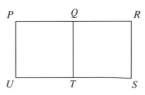

18. In the subtraction sum on the right a, b and c are digits, and a is less than b. What is the value of c?

$$\begin{array}{r} b\ a \\ -\ a\ b \\ \hline c\ 6 \end{array}$$

   A 3   B 4   C 5   D 6   E a number greater than 6

19. Two identical rectangular cards are glued together as shown to form an 'L' shape. The perimeter of this 'L' shape is 40 cm. What is the ratio of the lengths of the sides of one of the original cards?

   A 1:2   B 1:4   C 1:5   D 2:5   E more information required

20. How many of the statements in the box are true?

   A 0   B 1   C 2   D 3   E 4

   | None of these statements is true. |
   | Exactly one of these statements is true. |
   | Exactly two of these statements are true. |
   | All of these statements are true. |

21. If the square is completed with the letters A, B, C, D and E so that no row, column or either of the two main diagonal lines contains the same letter more than once, which letter should replace the asterisk?

   A   B   C   D   E

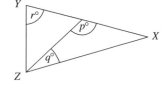

22. In a certain code, A = 1, B = 2, C = 3 etc. Words are encoded by multiplying together the values of their letters, so the code for SQUARE is $19 \times 17 \times 21 \times 1 \times 18 \times 5 = 610\,470$. Similarly, the code for RECTANGLE is 31 752 000. What is the code for TRIANGLE?

   A 2 116 800   B 2 721 600   C 19 051 200   D 25 401 600   E 52 920 000

23. In the diagram, triangle XYZ is isosceles, with $XY = XZ$. What is the value of r in terms of p and q?

   A $\frac{1}{2}(p - q)$ B $\frac{1}{2}(p + q)$ C $p - q$

   D $p + q$ E Impossible to determine

24. Jack dances clockwise around the Maypole, making one revolution every five seconds. Starting from a point diametrically opposite Jack's starting point, Jill dances anticlockwise, making one revolution every six seconds. How many times do they pass each other in the first minute?

   A 11   B 15   C 22   D 30   E 60

25. The diagram shows a unit cube coloured blue. Additional blue unit cubes are glued face-to-face to each of its six faces to form a three-dimensional "cross". If unit cubes coloured yellow are now glued face-to-face to all the spare faces of this cross, how many yellow unit cubes are required?

   A 6   B 18   C 24   D 30   E 36

Junior Challenge 2006

1. What is the value of 6002 − 2006?

   A 3994   B 3996   C 4000   D 4004   E 4006

2. Horatio the hamster likes to eat parts of clock faces. In which of these clock faces has the largest sum of numbers been eaten?

3. Among the children in a certain family, each child has at least one brother and at least one sister. What is the *smallest* possible number of children in the family?

   A 2   B 3   C 4   D 5   E 6

4. How many triangles of any size are there in this diagram?

   A 8   B 10   C 12   D 14   E 16

5. Euclid Gardens has 123 houses in it, numbered consecutively from 1 to 123. Houses 29 to 37 inclusive are knocked down to make space for a multi-storey car park. How many houses remain in Euclid Gardens?

   A 86   B 114   C 115   D 116   E 117

6. Each block shown in this tower is to have a number displayed on it. Some are already done. For each block above the bottom row, the number on it should be the sum of the numbers on the two blocks it stands upon.

   What number should replace *n*?

   A 3   B 6   C 10   D 11   E 13

7. What is the value of *x*?

   A 75   B 85   C 95   D 105   E 115

8. The diagram shows the net of a cube. Which edge meets the edge X when the net is folded to form the cube?

A   B   C   D   E

9. Four of these calculations give the same answer. Which is the odd one out?

A $2 \times \sqrt{64}$ B $22 - 2 \times 3$ C 2^4 D $5^2 - 3^2$ E $4 + 4 \times 2$

10. The diagram shows 7 identical coins which fit exactly inside a wooden frame. As a result each coin is prevented from sliding. What is the largest number of coins that may be removed one by one so that, at each stage, each remaining coin is still unable to slide?

A 0   B 1   C 2   D 3   E 4

11. Travelling by train from Edinburgh to London, I passed a sign saying "London 150 miles". After 7 more miles, I passed another sign saying "Edinburgh 250 miles". How far is it by train from Edinburgh to London?

A   407 miles   B   393 miles   C   257 miles   D   243 miles   E   157 miles

12.

| This sentence contains the letter e _____ times. |

seven   eight   nine   ten   eleven

How many of the five words above can be placed in the gap to make the sentence in the box true?

A   0   B   1   C   2   D   3   E   4

13. At the end of a hard day at the mine, the seven dwarves share out all their gold nuggets, making sure that they each get the same number of nuggets. If there are any left over, they are given to Snow White. Which number of nuggets would leave Snow White with the most?

A   300   B   400   C   500   D   600   E   700

14. In the rules of Association Football, Law 1 states that the field of play must be rectangular and have length from 100 to 130 yards, and width from 50 to 100 yards. What is the difference in area between the smallest possible field of play and the largest possible field of play?

A 1300 square yards B 5000 square yards C 8000 square yards
                    D 10 000 square yards   E 13 000 square yards

15. Which of these fractions does **not** simplify to $\frac{1}{4}$?

A $\dfrac{3942}{15768}$ B $\dfrac{4392}{17568}$ C $\dfrac{5796}{23184}$ D $\dfrac{6957}{31248}$ E $\dfrac{7956}{31824}$

16. The diagram shows an equilateral triangle with its corners at the mid-points of alternate sides of a regular hexagon. What fraction of the area of the hexagon is shaded?

    A $\frac{1}{2}$ B $\frac{1}{3}$ C $\frac{3}{8}$ D $\frac{4}{9}$ E $\frac{7}{12}$

17. In how many different ways can a row of five "on/off" switches be set so that no two adjacent switches are in the "off" position?

    A 5   B 10   C 11   D 13   E 15

18. In this magic square, which uses all whole numbers from 7 to 15 inclusive, each of the rows, columns and the two main diagonals has the same total. Which number replaces n in the completed square?

    A 8   B 9   C 10   D 11   E 12

19. Pinocchio's nose is 5cm long. Each time he tells a lie his nose doubles in length. After he has told nine lies, his nose will be roughly the same length as a:

    A domino   B tennis racquet   C snooker table   D tennis court   E football pitch

20. The sum of three different prime numbers is 40. What is the difference between the two biggest of these three numbers?

    A 8   B 12   C 16   D 20   E 24

21. Which one of the following shapes could not appear as the overlapping region of two identical squares?

    A equilateral triangle   B square   C kite
                      D heptagon   E regular octagon

22. A positive whole number less than 100 has remainder 2 when it is divided by 3, remainder 3 when it is divided by 4 and remainder 4 when it is divided by 5. What is its remainder when it is divided by 7?

    A 2   B 3   C 4   D 5   E 6

23. At a holiday camp, the ratio of boys to girls is 3:4 and the ratio of girls to adults is 5:7. What is the ratio of children to adults at the camp?

    A 4:5   B 5:4   C 12:7   D 15:28   E 21:20

24. Amrita has written down four whole numbers. If she chooses three of her numbers at a time and adds up each triple, she obtains totals of 115, 153, 169 and 181.
    What is the largest of Amrita's numbers?

    A 66   B 53   C 91   D 121   E 72

25. For how many positive values of n are both $\frac{1}{2}n$ and $2n$ three-digit whole numbers?

    A 0   B 150   C 200   D 300   E 500

Intermediate Challenge 1997

1. Which of the following numbers is not a perfect square?

   A 16   B 36   C 64   D 80   E 100

2. How is the number *ten million one hundred thousand and one* written?

   A 1001001   B 11000001   C 101000001 D 1010001   E 10100001

3. A fair die has just been rolled five times – giving scores of 1, 2, 3, 4, 5 in that order. How likely is it that the score on the next roll will be a 6?

   A no chance   B less than evens   C evens   D better than evens   E certain

4. A can of soup contains enough for three adults, or for five children. I have five cans of soup and fifteen children to feed. How many adults could I feed with what remains?

   A 0   B 3   C 5   D 6   E 15

5. What is the value of $\dfrac{67 \times (67 + 67)}{67}$?

   A 8978   B 134   C 68   D 67   E 2

6. The absorptive surface of the small intestine of a typical adult has an area of approximately 200 square metres. Which of the following has approximately the same area?

   A a dartboard   B a table tennis table   C a football
   pitch
                    D a golf course   E a tennis court

7. If the answers to the calculations shown below are placed in order of size, which will be in the middle?

   A $19 + 97$ B $19 - 97$ C 19×97 D $19 \div 97$ E 19^{97}

8. *GOOD NEWS!* Accidents in British homes involving tea-cosies went down from three in 1993 to nil in 1994. What percentage decrease was that?

   A 33.3%   B 66.6%   C 100%   D 300%   E Infinite %

9. The figure shows a net for a cube with a number on each face. When the cube is made, three faces meet at each vertex. The numbers on the three faces which meet at each vertex are multiplied together. What is the largest product obtained?

   A 40   B 60   C 72   D 90   E 120

10. Mickey Mouse wants to buy 20g of cheese. If cheese costs £3.41 per kilo, which calculation would Mickey need to do to find the cost, in pence, of 20g of cheese?

    A 3.41×20 B $3.41 \div 20$ C 3.41×0.02 D $341 \div 0.02$ E 341×0.02

11. In the quadrilateral $ABCD$, $\angle ABC = 90°$, $\angle BAD = 70°$ and $AB = BD = BC$. What is the size of $\angle BDC$?

    A 40°   B 50°   C 65°   D 70°   E 80°

12. Gill is nine years old this year so she was fascinated to discover that an integer is divisible by 9 precisely when the sum of its digits is also divisible by 9. If the six-digit number "1* 3456" is to be a multiple of 9, what must the missing digit be?

    A 2   B 3   C 5   D 8   E 9

13. What is half of 2^{20}?

    A 1^{10} B 1^{20} C 20   D 2^{10} E 2^{19}

14. "80% of the pupils asked preferred purple blazers, so purple blazers it is!", announced the Head triumphantly – conveniently forgetting to mention that 80% of pupils of the school had not even been asked. What percentage of pupils had actually told the Head that they preferred purple?

    A 16%   B 20%   C 40%   D 64%   E 80%

15. On the first day after the flood, half of Noah's animals escaped. On the second day one third of the remainder wandered off. On the third day one quarter of the rest hopped it. What fraction of Noah's original ménagerie was then left?

    A $\dfrac{1}{24}$ B $\dfrac{1}{4}$ C $\dfrac{1}{3}$ D $\dfrac{1}{2}$ E $\dfrac{3}{4}$

16. Thirty years ago Mike McNamara cycled 445.0 km in 12 hours – a new British men's record at that time. In the same time trial Beryl Burton (who died last year) completed 446.2 km. How much faster was Beryl Burton's average speed than Mike McNamara's (in metres per hour)?

    A 1.2   B 10   C 11   D 100   E 1200

17. The point O is the centre of a circle of radius 1 unit, OA, OC are radii, and $OABC$ is a square. What is the area of the shaded region (in square units)?

    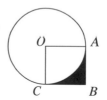

    A $1 - \dfrac{\pi}{4}$ B $1 - \dfrac{\pi}{2}$ C $\dfrac{(1 - \pi)}{4}$ D $2 - \dfrac{\pi}{2}$ E $2 - \dfrac{\pi}{4}$

18. Seven rolls weigh the same as four crumpets. Five scones weigh the same as six crumpets. If each crumpet weighs c grams, and each roll weighs r grams, and each scone weighs s grams, which of the following must be true?

    A $r < s < c$ B $s < r < c$ C $s < c < r$ D $c < s < r$ E $r < c < s$

19. You have to draw two (infinite) lines parallel to the x-axis, three (infinite) lines parallel to the y-axis, and four (infinite) lines parallel to the line $x = y$. What is the smallest possible total number of crossing points among the nine lines you draw?

    A 10   B 12   C 14   D 16   E 18

20. In the right-angled triangle ABC, $BD = 8$, $AD = 10$ and $AD = DC$. What is the area of triangle ADC?

    A 80   B 40   C 30   D 24   E 20

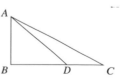

21. If $a = b - c, b = c - d$, and $c = d - a$, then $\dfrac{a}{b} + \dfrac{b}{c} + \dfrac{c}{d} + \dfrac{d}{a}$ equals

     A 1   B $\dfrac{1}{2}$ C 0   D $-\dfrac{1}{2}$ E -1

22. In triangle PQR the point N lies on the side PR, and the point M lies on the side PQ. The segment QN bisects the angle PQR, and MN is parallel to QR. Which of the following statements follows logically from this given information?

     A $MN = \tfrac{1}{2}QR$ B $MN = MQ$ C $MN = NP$ D $MN = RN$ E Statements A-D

                                                            may all be

     false

23. The square $ABCD$ is inscribed in a circle of radius 1. Semicircles are drawn with diameters AB, BC, CD, DA as shown, and the parts of these semicircles which lie *outside* the original circle are shaded. What is the total area of these four shaded regions?

     A $3\pi + 2$ B 2   C π D 1   E $\dfrac{\pi}{2}$

24. A *regular dodecahedron* is a polyhedron with twelve faces, each of which is regular pentagon. A space diagonal of the dodecahedron is a line segment which joins two vertices of the dodecahedron which do not lie in the same face. How many space diagonals are there in the dodecahedron?

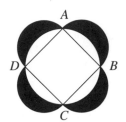

     A 100   B 110   C 170   D 200   E 220

25. A crossnumber is like a crossword, except that all the answers are numbers instead of words (with one digit in each square, and no answer starting with the digit zero). How many different solutions are there to the crossnumber on the right?

CLUES

ACROSS
1. Prime
3. Square
5. Prime

DOWN
1. Prime
2. Square
4. Square

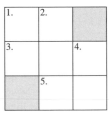

     A 0   B 1   C 2   D 3   E more than three

Intermediate Challenge 1998

1. One quarter of a number is 24. What is one third of the original number?

   A 6   B 8   C 32   D 72   E 96

2. 6% of 6 plus 8% of 8 equals

   A 0.14   B 1   C 1.4   D 1.98   E 2

3. Starting at A, a point on a fixed circle with centre O, I first move anticlockwise one quarter of the way round the circle to a point W, hop across to X – the opposite end of the diameter through W, then travel one fifth of the way round the circle clockwise to the point Y before hopping across to Z, the point at the opposite end of the diameter through Y. How big is $\angle AOZ$?

   A 18°   B 22°   C 162°   D 198°   E 270°

4. Which fraction is the odd one out?

   A $\dfrac{1 + 4}{7 + 4}$ B $\dfrac{20}{140}$ C $\dfrac{0.2}{1.4}$ D $\dfrac{1 \div 11}{7 \div 11}$ E $\dfrac{8}{56}$

5. J is the set of High Court judges; K is the set of living things beginning with K; L is the set of all living creatures; M is the set of brilliant mathematicians. Kevin is a very ordinary kangaroo. In which of the five regions A-E of the diagram does Kevin belong?

   A   B   C   D   E

6. $ABCD$ is a square with sides of length 9cm. How many points (inside or outside the square) are equidistant from B and from C, and are exactly 6cm from A?

   A 0   B 1   C 2   D 3   E more than 3

7. Each person's *birthday product* is obtained by multiplying the day of the month in which they were born by the number of the month in which they were born, and then multiplying the answer by the year in which they were born. Here are five English queens and their birthdays. Which of them has the same birthday product as someone born today?

   A Mary 1, 18 February 1518   B Elizabeth 1, 7 September 1533
   C Anne, 6 February 1665   D Victoria, 24 May 1819
   E Elizabeth 11, 21 April 1926

8. How large will an angle of $2\frac{1}{2}°$ appear to be if you enlarge it by looking through a stack of five magnifying glasses, each one of which magnifies by a factor of 2?

   A $2\frac{1}{2}°$ B $12\frac{1}{2}°$ C 25°   D 40°   E 80°

9. What is the total number of letters in all the incorrect options for this question?

   A eleven   B twenty two   C thirty three   D forty four   E fifty five

10. On four tests, each marked out of 100, my average was 85. What is the lowest mark I could have scored on any one test?

    A 0   B 40   C 60   D 81   E 85

11. The *World Wide Fund for Nature* estimates that 54 acres of Brazilian rainforest are destroyed every minute of every day. Approximately how many acres are lost each week?

A 50 000   B 80 000   C 200 000   D 500 000   E 2 000 000

12. If $C°$ Celsius is the same temperature as $F°$ Fahrenheit, then $F = \left(\frac{9}{5}\right)C + 32$. To avoid working with fractions and awkward numbers, some people use the approximate formula $F' = 2C + 30$. What is the temperature in degrees Celsius when the approximate formula gives an answer which is too large by 1?

A 5   B 9   C 10   D 12   E 15

13. I fold a piece of paper in half, then in half again before cutting a shape from the folded paper as shown. When I unfold the paper, what do I see?

A   B   C   D   E

14. In a sponsored "Animal Streak" the cheetah ran at 90km/hr while the snail slimed along at 20 hr/km. The cheetah kept going for 18 seconds. Roughly how long would the snail take to cover the same distance?

A 9 months   B 9 weeks   C 9 days   D 9 hours   E 9 minutes

15. Wallace and Gromit are waiting in a queue. There are x people behind Wallace, who is y places in front of Gromit. If there are n people in front of Gromit, how long is the queue?

A $n - x + y + 2$ B $n + x - y$ C $n - x + y - 1$ D $n + x - y + 1$ E $n - x + y$

16. I made just enough sticky treacle mixture to exactly fill a square tin of side 12 inches. But all I could find were two $8\frac{1}{2}$ inch square tins. How well would the mixture fit?

A easily   B just (with a teeny bit of room to spare)   C an exact fit
D nearly (with a small overflow)   E no way (major overflow)

17. Which of the four triangles W, X, Y, Z are right-angled?

A only W B W and X C X and Z D Y and W E Y and Z

18. The integers from 1 to 20 are listed below in such a way that the sum of each adjacent pair is a prime number. Missing numbers are marked as *s.

20, *, 16, 15, 4, *, 12, *, 10, 7, 6, *, 2, 17, 14, 9, 8, 5, 18, *.

Which number goes in the place which is underlined?

A 1   B 3   C 11   D 13   E 19

19. *ABCDE* is a regular pentagon. *FAB* is a straight line and *FA* = *AB*. What is the ratio $x : y : z$?

    A 1 : 2 : 3   B 2 : 2 : 3   C 2 : 3 : 4

    D 3 : 4 : 5   E 3 : 4 : 6

20. The total length of all the edges of a cube is *L* cm. If the surface area of the cube has the same numerical value *L* cm^2 what is its volume in cm^3?

    A 1   B *L*   C 2   D L^3 E 8

21. A piece of thin card in the shape of an equilateral triangle with side 3 cm and a circular piece of thin card of radius 1 cm are glued together so that their centres coincide. How long is the outer perimeter of the resulting 2-dimensional shape (in cm)?

    A 2π B $6 + \pi$ C 9   D 3π E $9 + 2\pi$

22. Shape A is made from 6 unit squares; shape B is made from 8, C from 4, 0 from 8 and E from 3 unit squares. For four of these shapes, four exact copies can be fitted together to make a rectangle. Which is the odd one out?

    A   B   C   D   E

23. In this unusual game of noughts and crosses the first player to form a line of three Os or three Xs *loses*. It is X's turn. Where should she place her cross to make sure that she does not lose?

    A   B   C   D   E

A	O	B
C	X	D
E	X	O

24. Each of the sides of this regular octagon has length 2cm. What is the difference between the area of the shaded region and the area of the unshaded region (in cm^2)?

    A 0   B 1   C 1.5   D 2   E $2\sqrt{2}$

25. A square is inscribed in a 3-4-5 right-angled triangle as shown. What fraction of the triangle does it occupy?

    A $\dfrac{12}{25}$ B $\dfrac{24}{49}$ C $\dfrac{1}{2}$ D $\dfrac{25}{49}$ E $\dfrac{13}{25}$

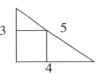

Intermediate Challenge 1999

1. Which of these numbers is biggest?

    A 19×99 B 199×9 C 199^9 D $1^9 \times 9^9$ E 1^{999}

2. A sheet of A4 size paper (297mm × 210mm) is folded once and then laid flat on the table. Which of these shapes could not be made?

    A [square]   B [right triangle]   C [square]   D [right triangle]   E [rectangle]

3. A certain company offers "750 hours of free Internet use for new subscribers". On closer inspection it becomes clear that this time must be used during the new subscriber's first month of membership!

    What is the maximum number of hours in any one month of the year?

    A 168   B 692   C 720   D 744   E 750

4. Ima Divvy used her calculator and multiplied a number by 20 instead of by 2. What could she now do to obtain the correct answer?

    A divide by 20   B divide by 40   C multiply by 10
                D multiply by 0.5   E multiply by 0.1

5. 30 ÷ 0.2 equals

    A 1.5   B 6   C 15   D 150   E 600

6. In Britain in 1996 we consumed on average 9.6 kg of bananas per person per year (that is, around 60 bananas each). In some parts of Africa, the consumption of bananas is as high as 250 kg of bananas per person per year. Roughly how many bananas is that?

    A 4 or 5 a day   B 1 or 2 a day   C 4 or 5 a week
    D 1 or 2 a week   E 4 or 5 a month

7. Which is smallest?

    A $\dfrac{(2 + 3)}{(4 + 6)}$ B $\dfrac{(2 \div 3)}{(4 \div 6)}$ C $\dfrac{23}{46}$ D $\dfrac{(2 - 3)}{(4 - 6)}$ E $\dfrac{(2 \times 3)}{(4 \times 6)}$

8. In the diagram $PQ = PR = RS$.
    What is the size of angle x?

    A 54°   B 72°   C 90°   D 108°   E 144°

    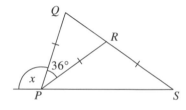

9. It is evening and Meg, who is 1m tall, casts a shadow of length 3m. If Meg stands on her brother's shoulders, which are 1.5m above the ground, how long a shadow will she and her brother cast?

    A 3m   B 4.5m   C 5.5m   D 6.5m   E 7.5m

10. In March 1998 a book called "*The Shadow of the East*" was returned to a library in Sussex. It had been borrowed on January 3rd 1924! The library charges a fine of 60p per week for overdue books. Approximately how big a fine should the person who returned the book have paid?

    A £45   B £180   C £230   D £2200   E £16 000

11. "20% off everything", screamed the sale posters. I paid £60. What would I have paid before the sale?

    A £60   B £66   C £72   D £75   E £80

12. In a right angled triangle the two shorter sides have lengths 10cm and 5cm. Which of the following approximations is closest to the length of the hypotenuse?

    A 11cm   B 11.5cm   C 12cm   D 12.5cm   E 13cm

13. The diagram shows a semicircle containing a circle which touches the circumference of the semicircle and goes through its centre. What fraction of the semicircle is shaded?

    A $\dfrac{2}{3}$ B $\dfrac{1}{2}$ C $\dfrac{1}{\pi}$ D $\dfrac{2}{\pi}$ E $\dfrac{3}{\pi}$

14. Which of the following statements is false?

    A an octagon has twenty diagonals   B a hexagon has nine diagonals
    C a hexagon has four more diagonals than a pentagon
    D a pentagon has the same number of diagonals as it has sides
    E a quadrilateral has twice as many diagonals as it has sides

15. A pencil AB lying on a table is given a half-turn about the end B (so that A moves to A') and then a half-turn about A' (so that B moves to B'). The point C on the pencil is one third of the way from A to B.
What is the ratio of the total distances moved by A and by C?

    A 3:1   B 3:2   C 1:1   D 2:3   E 1:3

16. On the right are three statements. Exactly which ones are true?   (i) 3^{10} is even   (ii) 3^{10} is odd   (iii) 3^{10} is square

    A (i) only   B (ii) only   C (iii) only   D (i) and (iii)   E (ii) and (iii)

17. The three circles in the diagram have the same centre and have radii 3cm, 4cm and 5cm. What percentage of the area of the largest circle is shaded?

    A 20%   B 25%   C 28%   D 30%   E $33\frac{1}{3}$%

18. Seventy pupils (37 boys and 33 girls) are divided into two groups, with forty pupils in Group I and thirty pupils in Group II. How many more boys are there in Group I than there are girls in Group II?

A 4   B 7   C 8   D 9   E more information needed

19. Four *wiggles* are the same as three *woggles*; two *woggles* are the same as five *waggles*, and six *waggles* are the same as one *wuggle*. Which is smallest?

A 1 *wuggle*   B 2 *woggles*   C 3 *waggles*   D 4 *wiggles*   E two have the same value

20. Inspector Remorse estimates that he can solve the average murder in x hours, a bank robbery in half that time, and a car theft in one third of the time he takes to solve a bank robbery. How many hours would he expect to take in solving two murders, six car thefts and four bank robberies?

A 3x B 5x C 6x D 7x E 12x

21. When exactly is the value of the product $\left(1 + \frac{1}{2}\right)\left(1 + \frac{1}{3}\right)\left(1 + \frac{1}{4}\right)\ldots\left(1 + \frac{1}{n}\right)$ equal to an integer?

A when n is odd   B when n is even   C when n is a multiple of 3
D always   E never

22. In the *Soft Boulder Café* each table has 3 legs, each chair has 4 legs and all the customers and the three members of staff have two legs each. There are four chairs at each table. At a certain time, three-quarters of the chairs are occupied by customers and there are 206 legs altogether in the café. How many *chairs* does the café have?

A 20   B 24   C 28   D 32   E 36

23. In the star shown here the sum of the four numbers in any "line" is the same for each of the five "lines". The five missing numbers are 9, 10, 11, 12 and 13. Which number is represented by K?

A 9   B 10   C 11   D 12   E 13

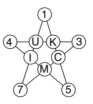

24. The Queen of Hearts has lost her tarts! She is sure that those knaves who have not eaten the tarts will tell her the truth and that the guilty knaves will tell lies. When questioned, the five knaves declare:

K1 *"One of us ate them."*   K2 *"Two of us ate them."*   K3 *"Three of us ate them."*

K4: *"Four of us ate them."*   K5: *"Five of us ate them."*

How many of the knaves were honest?

A 1   B 2   C 3   D 4   E 5

25. A rectangular sheet of paper with sides 1 and $\sqrt{2}$ has been folded once as shown, so that one corner just meets the opposite long edge.

What is the value of the length d?

A $\frac{1}{2}$ B $\sqrt{2} - 1$ C $\frac{7}{16}$ D $\sqrt{3} - \sqrt{2}$ E $\frac{\sqrt{2}}{3}$

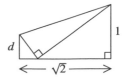

Intermediate Challenge 2000

1. 567 is multiplied by 3489. What is the units digit of the answer?

    A 1   B 3   C 5   D 7   E 9

2. An ice cream stall sells vanilla, strawberry and chocolate ice creams. The pie chart illustrates the sales of ice cream for last Saturday. The number of vanilla and the number of chocolate ice creams sold were the same. The stall sold 60 strawberry ice creams. How many chocolate ice creams were sold?

    A 90   B 99   C 100   D 120   E 135

3. Which is the largest of these fractions?

    A $\dfrac{7}{15}$ B $\dfrac{3}{7}$ C $\dfrac{11}{23}$ D $\dfrac{4}{9}$ E $\dfrac{6}{11}$

4. In Worcestershire, Wyre Piddle is 12km south of the village of North Piddle and Abbotts Morton is 12km east of North Piddle. What is the direction of Abbotts Morton from Wyre Piddle?

    A South East   B South West   C North East   D North West   E West

5. In a magic square, each row, each column and both main diagonals have the same total. In the partially completed magic square shown, what number should replace x?

    A 15   B 18   C 21   D 24   E 27

6. Granny has been having a smashing time. Yesterday she had 12 cups and 10 matching saucers, but this morning she dropped a tray holding one third of the cups and half the saucers, breaking all of those on the tray. How many of her cups are now without saucers?

    A 1   B 3   C 4   D 5   E 6

7. Given that x and y are positive whole numbers and $x^2 + 2 = y^3$, which of the following is a possible value of x?

    A 2   B 3   C 4   D 5   E 6

8. In the triangle ABC, $AD = BD = CD$. What is the size of angle BAC?

    A 60°   B 75°   C 90°   D 120°

    E more information is needed

9. Leap years normally occur every four years. However, years at the turn of a century are leap years only if they are multiples of 400. Therefore this year, 2000, is a leap year, but the year 1900 was not a leap year. How many leap years will there be between 2001 and 3001?

    A 240   B 242   C 248   D 249   E 250

10. The average (mean) weight of five giant dates was 50g. Kate ate one and the average (mean) weight of the four remaining dates was 40g. What was the weight of the date that Kate ate?

     A   10 g   B   50 g   C   60 g   D   90 g   E   more information is needed

11. My bargain settee cost me £240 in a sale offering 25% reductions on all items. How much did I save?

     A   £25   B   £40   C   £60   D   £80   E   £100

12. Timmy, Tammy and Tommy all have tummy ache! They all set off separately to visit their doctor, leaving their homes at exactly the same time. Timmy cycles the 8 km to the surgery at an average speed of 20 km/hr; Tammy walks the 1.2 km to the surgery at an average speed of 4 km/hr and Tommy drives the 16.5 km to the surgery at an average speed of 45 km/hr. In what order do they arrive at the surgery?

     A   Tommy, Timmy, Tammy   B   Timmy, Tommy, Tammy   C   Timmy, Tammy, Tommy

           D   Tammy, Timmy, Tommy   E   Tammy, Tommy, Timmy

13. The diagram shows two rectangles which enclose five regions. What is the largest number of regions which can be enclosed by any two rectangles drawn on a sheet of paper?

     A   10   B   9   C   8   D   7   E   6

14. The ratio $a : b = 2 : 3$ and the ratio $a : c = 3 : 4$. What is the ratio $b : c$?

     A   1 : 8   B   1 : 2   C   8 : 9   D   9 : 8   E   2 : 1

15. In how many whole numbers between 100 and 999 is the middle digit equal to the sum of the other two digits?

     A   28   B   36   C   45   D   50   E   55

16. The pattern 123451234512345... is continued to form a 2000-digit number. What is the sum of all 2000 digits?

     A   6000   B   7500   C   30 000   D   60 000   E   75 000

17. Baldrick can afford to buy either 6 parsnips and 7 turnips or else 8 parsnips and 4 turnips. Both options leave him with no change whatsoever. If, however, he bought only his beloved turnips, how many could he afford?

     A   11   B   12   C   13   D   16   E   25

18. The number $3^4 \times 4^5 \times 5^6$ is written out in full. How many zeros are there at the end of the number?

     A   none   B   4   C   5   D   6   E   more than 6

19. The product of Mary's age in years on her last birthday and her age now in complete months is 1800. How old was Mary on her last birthday?

     A   9   B   10   C   12   D   15   E   18

20. The populations of five cities A, B, C, D, E in 1988 and 1998 are shown on these scales.

1998 population in thousands

1988 population in thousands

Which of the five cities showed the largest percentage increase in population from 1988 to 1998?

A   B   C   D   E

21. A wire in the shape of an equilateral triangle with sides of length 9 cm is placed flat on a piece of paper. A pencil is held in the hole at the centre of a disc of radius 1 cm, and the disc is rolled all the way around the outside of the wire, and then all the way around the inside of the wire. What shape is drawn by the pencil?

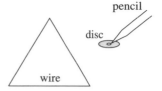

A   B   C   D   E

22. One hundred and twenty students take an exam which is marked out of 100 (with no fractional marks). No three students are awarded the same mark. What is the smallest possible number of pairs of students who are awarded the same mark?

A 9   B 10   C 19   D 20   E 60

23. *ABCDEFGHI* is a regular nine-sided polygon (called a 'nonagon' or 'enneagon'). What is the size of angle *FAE*?

A 10°   B 20°   C 30°   D 40°   E 50°

24. Jasmine spends exactly £120 on three types of plants: poisoned ivy, deadly nightshade and triffids. Poisoned ivy plants cost £2 each, deadly nightshade plants cost £9 each and triffids cost £12 each. She buys twenty plants in total, including at least one of each type. How many triffids did she buy?

A 1   B 2   C 3   D 4   E more information is needed

25. The large circles in each figure have the same radius. Which shaded area is the greatest?

A   B   C   D   E

Intermediate Challenge 2001

1. Between which of the following pairs of numbers is there the greatest difference?

   A −3, 8   B −5, −13   C 1, 11   D 4, −5   E −6, −15

2. A tourist attraction, which opens every day, needs 30 000 visitors per day on average to break even. Last week there were 120 000 visitors. What is the number of visitors needed this week to break even over the two-week period?

   A 43 000   B 90 000   C 180 000   D 210 000   E 300 000

3. Which of the following is midway between $\frac{1}{4}$ and $\frac{1}{8}$?

   A $\frac{3}{16}$ B $\frac{1}{6}$ C $\frac{5}{24}$ D $\frac{1}{5}$ E $\frac{7}{32}$

4. Old Martha has 5 children, each of whom has 4 children, each of whom has 3 children, each of whom is childless. How many descendants does Old Martha have?

   A 12   B 20   C 25   D 60   E 85

5. In the diagram the lines PQ and SR are parallel, as are the lines PS and QT. What is the value of x?

   A 139   B 138   C 124   D 98   E 97

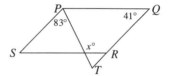

6. $2001 = 3 \times 23 \times 29$. Which of the following numbers is also the product of exactly three distinct prime numbers?

   A 45   B 60   C 91   D 105   E 330

7. A ream of paper (500 sheets) is 5·4 cm thick. What is the thickness of a single sheet, correct to one significant figure?

   A 1 mm   B 0·5 mm   C 0·1 mm   D 0·05 mm   E 0·01 mm

8. The diagram shows a right-angled isosceles triangle XYZ which circumscribes a square PQRS. The area of triangle XYZ is x. What is the area of square PQRS?

   A $\frac{4x}{9}$ B $\frac{x}{2}$ C $\frac{4x}{5}$ D $\frac{2x}{5}$ E $\frac{2x}{3}$

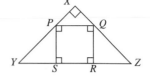

9. Which of the following is the best estimate for the number of seconds which have elapsed since the start of the year 2000?

   A 3×10^4 B 3×10^5 C 3×10^6 D 3×10^7 E 3×10^8

10. Equal regular pentagons are placed together to form a ring in the manner shown. The diagram shows the first three pentagons.

    How many *more* are needed to complete the ring?

    A 6   B 7   C 8   D 9   E 10

11. A square card printed with the letter N is held horizontally, as shown in the diagram, where the arrow indicates the direction of North. The card is turned over by rotating it through 180° about an axis running from East to West, and then turned over by rotating it through 180° about an axis running from North-East to South-West.
How does the diagram on the card now look to a person facing North?

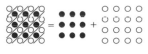

12. A long-sleeve shirt has 8 front buttons and 2 cuff buttons; a short-sleeve shirt has 6 front buttons and no cuff buttons. The factory which makes 'Slimboy Shirts' uses 10 times as many front buttons as cuff buttons. What is the ratio of long-sleeve shirts to short-sleeve shirts produced by the factory?

   A 4 : 1   B 4 : 3   C 2 : 3   D 3 : 4   E 1 : 2

13. The diagram shows that $1 + 3 + 5 + 7 + 5 + 3 + 1 = 3^2 + 4^2$.
What is $1 + 3 + 5 + \ldots + 1999 + 2001 + 1999 + \ldots + 5 + 3 + 1$?

   A $999^2 + 1000^2$ B $1000^2 + 1001^2$ C $1999^2 + 2000^2$
       D $2000^2 + 2001^2$ E none of these

14. A square patchwork quilt is made by joining four square pieces of cloth like this ◺. each piece coloured grey and white as shown. Only edges of the same colour are sewn together. How many different quilt patterns are possible? (Two patterns are considered to be the same if one can be rotated to look exactly like the other.)

   A 3   B 4   C 5   D 6   E 8

15. How many of the numbers

       $3\sqrt{11}$ $4\sqrt{7}$ $5\sqrt{5}$ $6\sqrt{3}$ $7\sqrt{2}$
   are greater than 10?

   A 1   B 2   C 3   D 4   E 5

16. The Pythagoras Patisserie sells triangular cakes at 39p each and square buns at 23p each. For her party, Helen spent exactly £5.12 on an assortment of these cakes and buns. How many items in total did she buy?

   A 15   B 16   C 17   D 18   E 19

17. Albert Einstein was standing on the station platform thinking about relativity when he noticed that he could see two station clocks. Each clock was digital, showing only hours and minutes. He observed that the display on one clock changed to the next minute 10 seconds before the correct time, whereas the display on the other clock changed to the next minute 10 seconds after the correct time. For what fraction of the day did the clocks show the same time?

   A $\dfrac{1}{6}$ B $\dfrac{1}{3}$ C $\dfrac{2}{3}$ D $\dfrac{5}{6}$ E $\dfrac{7}{6}$

18. An athlete covers three consecutive miles by walking the first mile, running the second and cycling the third. He runs twice as fast as he walks, and he cycles one and a half times as fast as he runs. He takes ten minutes longer than he would do if he cycled the three miles. How long does he take by walking, running and cycling?

A 60 min   B 42 min   C 36 min   D 30 min   E 22 min

19. The diagram shows a large rectangle composed of nine identical smaller rectangles. Both the length and breadth of each of these smaller rectangles are whole numbers of centimetres. Which of the following could be the area of the large rectangle?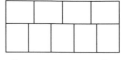

A 450 cm^2 B 630 cm^2 C 1260 cm^2 D 1440 cm^2 E 1620 cm^2

20. In how many different ways can seven different numbers be chosen from the numbers 1 to 9 inclusive so that the seven numbers have a total which is a multiple of 3?

A fewer than 10   B 10   C 11   D 12   E more than 12

21. Given that x is positive and less than 1, which of the following numbers is the largest?

A $x^2 + x$ B x^2 C x^3 D $x^3 + x^2$ E x^4

22. A regular tetrahedron with edges of length 6 cm has each corner cut off to produce the solid shown. The triangular faces are all equilateral triangles, but not necessarily all the same size. What is the total length of the edges of the resulting solid?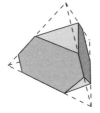

A 28 cm   B 30 cm   C 36 cm

          D 48 cm   E more information needed

23. For how many values of n are both n and $\dfrac{n+3}{n-1}$ integers?

A 7   B 6   C 4   D 3   E 0

24. A 4 by 4 'antimagic square' is an arrangement of the numbers 1 to 16 inclusive in a square, so that the totals of each of the four rows and four columns and two main diagonals are ten consecutive numbers in some order. The diagram shows an incomplete antimagic square. When it is completed, what number will replace the asterisk?

4	5	7	14
6	13	3	*
11	12	9	
10			

A 1   B 2   C 8   D 15   E 16

25. *AB* is a diameter of a circle of radius 1 cm. Two circular arcs of equal radius are drawn with centres *A* and *B*. These arcs meet on the circle, as shown. What is the shaded area?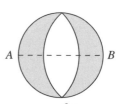

A $\dfrac{\pi}{2}$ cm^2 B 1 cm^2 C $(\pi - 1)$ cm^2 D 2 cm^2 E $\dfrac{2\pi}{3}$ cm^2

Intermediate Challenge 2002

1. Which of the following numbers could replace $\square$ so that the value of $\dfrac{\square}{5}$ lies between 3 and 4?

   A 3.2   B 9   C 14   D 19   E 24

2. Which of the following has the greatest value?

   A 0.3 × 7   B 0.5 × 5   C 0.2 × 11   D 0.09 × 30   E 0.026 × 100

3. Alice's room is furnished with three-legged stools and four-legged chairs. There are 17 legs in all (excluding Alice's!). How many three-legged stools are there?

   A 1   B 2   C 3   D 4   E 5

4. The figure shows an equilateral triangle divided into small equilateral triangles, all equal. What is the lowest number of small triangles which must now be shaded to produce a figure which has a line of symmetry?

   A 2   B 3   C 4   D 5   E 6

5. My local greengrocery, 'Apples and Pears' (known as 'AP' for short), charges 24p for the first apple bought, 23p for the second, 22p for the third, and so on, each apple costing 1p less than the one before. How much change should I receive if I buy 9 apples and I give the shopkeeper £2?

   A 24p   B 23p   C 22p   D 21p   E 20p

6. The *letter-product* of a number is obtained by multiplying the number by the number of letters in the corresponding word. For example, the letter-product of 5 is 20, since there are 4 letters in the word 'five' and 5 × 4 = 20. Which of the following has the largest letter-product?

   A 6   B 7   C 8   D 9   E 10

7. In square metres, what area of this pennant is shaded grey?

   A 50   B 54   C 57   D 60   E 72

8. What is the value of $2^{10} - 10^2$?

   A −1000   B −80   C 0   D 924   E 1000

9. A *Langford number* is one in which each digit of the number occurs twice; the digits 1 are separated by one other digit, the digits 2 are separated by two others, and so on. Which of the following is a Langford number?

   A 12142334   B 41312432   C 14132342   D 32432141   E 31213244

10. Anna has 3 brothers and 5 sisters. Her brother Tom has S sisters and B brothers. What is the value of $S \times B$?

    A 8   B 10   C 12   D 15   E 18

11. The standard Fibonacci sequence 1, 1, 2, 3, 5, 8, 13, ... begins with two 1s, and each later number in the sequence is the sum of the previous two numbers. Other Fibonacci-like sequences can be constructed by starting with any two numbers a and b (not necessarily 1 and 1) and using the same rule for creating the other numbers in the sequence. What is the first term of the Fibonacci-like sequence whose second term is 4 and whose fifth term is 22?

     A   2   B   3   C   4   D   5   E   6

12. In the game Four-in-a-Row, two players take it in turns to place counters on the 5 × 5 board. The winner is the first player to have four adjacent counters in a line across or down (but not diagonally).

It is Black's turn to play next. Where should she play her fourth counter to be certain of winning on her fifth turn whatever White plays?

     A   B   C   D   E

13. Granny has made another of her special super-heavy giant rock cakes. At her birthday party, five of the guests tried to guess the weight of the cake. Their guesses were 5040g, 5060g, 5110g, 5120g, and 5150g. Actually, none of them was right. Only two were more than 30 grams out, and they were out by 70g and 90g. What was the weight of the cake?

     A   5070g   B   5080g   C   5090g   D   5110g   E   5130g

14. I have four rectangular pieces of thin hardboard whose dimensions (in cm) are 55 × 85, 65 × 75, 65 × 85 and 90 × 105. Without bending the hardboard, how many of these can I get through an open rectangular window measuring 60 cm × 80 cm?

     A   0   B   1   C   2   D   3   E   4

15. Jack had five cards in a pile on a table. He gave me the top card, and then placed the next card at the bottom of the pile; then he gave me the next one on the top and placed the next one after that at the bottom of his pile. He continued like this until he had given me all of the cards. I looked down and to my surprise found that Jack had given me the cards in order: Ace, 2, 3, 4, 5. In what order (top to bottom) did Jack originally have the cards in the pile on the table?

     A   Ace,2,3,4,5   B   Ace,4,2,5,3   C   Ace,5,2,3,4   D   Ace,5,2,4,3   E   Ace,5,3,4,2

16. The diagram, which is not drawn accurately, shows a parallelogram inside a triangle. The marked lengths are equal. What is the value of x?

     A 60   B 75   C 90   D 120   E more information needed

17. I walk to the bike shop at 3 miles per hour and cycle back along the same route at 12 miles per hour. What is my average speed, in miles per hour, for the time I am actually travelling on the route?

     A   3.75   B   4.8   C   6   D   8   E   9

18. What fraction of the rectangle $PQRS$ is shaded?

     A $\dfrac{16}{81}$ B $\dfrac{4}{9}$ C $\dfrac{2}{9}$ D $\dfrac{1}{8}$ E $\dfrac{1}{9}$

19. A cylindrical can contains lemonade, shown shaded on the diagram in which *XY* is a diameter. What fraction of the volume of the can is filled with lemonade?

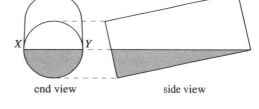

end view   side view

   A just below a quarter

   B just above a quarter

   C exactly a quarter

   D just below a half

   E exactly a half

20. Which of the following scores is it impossible to achieve in this challenge? (Note that if two or more answers are given to a question then they are treated as one incorrect answer.)

   A 126   B 127   C 128   D 129   E 130

21. This year started on a Tuesday. In which of the following years will each date fall on the same day of the week as it falls this year?

   A 2008   B 2009   C 2012   D 2013   E 2014

22. The diagram shows an irregular hexagon with interior angles all equal to 120° made by cutting the corners off a piece of card in the shape of an equilateral triangle with sides of length 20 units. An identical hexagon could also be made by cutting the corners off a different equilateral triangle: what is the side length of this triangle?

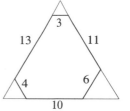

   A 23   B 25   C 27   D 29   E 31

23. A heptagon is a seven-sided polygon. What is the greatest number of the following properties that a single heptagon can possibly possess?

Its interior angles add up to 900 degrees.	All its sides are equal.
It has exactly four acute interior angles.	It has exactly one line of symmetry.
It has no obtuse interior angles.	

   A 1   B 2   C 3   D 4   E 5

24. A digital clock uses two digits to display hours, two digits to display minutes and two digits to display seconds, e.g. 10:23:42. How many times between 10:00:00 and 11:00:00 on the same morning are all six digits different?

   A 120   B 240   C 360   D 480   E 600

25. Given that $x = \dfrac{111110}{111111}$, $y = \dfrac{222221}{222223}$, $z = \dfrac{333331}{333334}$, which of the following statements is correct?

   A $x < y < z$ B $x < z < y$ C $y < z < x$ D $z < x < y$ E $y < x < z$

Intermediate Challenge 2003

1. What is the value of 3 divided by $\frac{1}{2}$?

    A $\frac{1}{6}$ B $\frac{2}{3}$ C $1\frac{1}{2}$ D $4\frac{1}{2}$ E 6

2. Four of these tiles may be put side by side so that they simultaneously spell two imperial units of length. Which tile is left out?

    A $\dfrac{E}{D}$ B $\dfrac{I}{A}$ C $\dfrac{L}{R}$ D $\dfrac{K}{C}$ E $\dfrac{M}{Y}$

3. You are given that $2786 \times 231 = 643566$. What is the value of $643566 \div 27 \cdot 86$?

    A 23100   B 2310   C 231   D 23.1   E 2.31

4. The coach of the Irish hockey team has a maximum speed of 60 miles per hour. If it travels at this speed for two hours, roughly how many kilometres does it travel?

    A 120   B 160   C 200   D 240   E 280

5. What is the value of 2003^2?

    A 4009   B 400 009   C 401 209   D 4 000 009   E 4 012 009

6. Think of a number, double it, then add 3. Multiply your answer by 4 and from this take away 5. Now also take away the number you first thought of. No matter what your first number was, your answer will be a multiple of:

    A 2   B 3   C 5   D 7   E 11

7. Last year a newspaper reported that Turkish football team Sarigol Municipality transferred four of its players in return for a fee of 225 sacks of cement, needed to repair their stadium. At the same rate of exchange, how many sacks of cement would be the transfer fee for a full team of eleven players and one reserve?

    A 233   B 450   C 675   D 900   E 2700

8. Lines AB and CD are parallel and $BC = BD$. Given that x is an acute angle not equal to 60°, how many *other* angles in this diagram are equal to x?

    A 1   B 2   C 3   D 4   E 5

    not to scale

9. It has been estimated that the mass of insects caught by spiders in a year in the UK is equal to the mass of the human population of the UK. Assuming this population is 60 million and the average mass of a human is 70 kg, what is the mass, in tonnes, of insects caught by spiders per year in the UK?

    A 4.2   B 42   C 4200   D 420 000   E 4 200 000

10. The time shown on a digital clock is 5:55. How many minutes will pass before the clock next shows a time for which all the digits are the same?

    A 71   B 255   C 316   D 377   E 436

11. Which of the following fractions is in the middle when they are written in numerical order?

    A $\frac{4}{7}$ B $\frac{5}{8}$ C $\frac{3}{4}$ D $\frac{7}{11}$ E $\frac{8}{13}$

12. Each edge of a cube is coloured either red or black. If every face of the cube has at least one black edge, what is the smallest possible number of black edges?

    A 2   B 3   C 4   D 5   E 6

13. What is the maximum number of pieces with the shape T which can be placed within the 5 × 5 grid shown, without overlapping, and with their edges along the lines of the grid?

    A 3   B 4   C 5   D 6   E 7

T

14. In the diagram, ∠*MON* = 130°. The reflection of *OP* in *OM* is *OQ* and the reflection of *OP* in *ON* is *OR*. What is the size of ∠*QOR*?

    A 100°   B 120°   C 140°   D 150°   E 160°

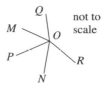

not to scale

15. Each interior angle of a particular polygon is an obtuse angle which is a whole number of degrees. What is the greatest number of sides the polygon could have?

    A 90   B 179   C 180   D 359   E 360

16. After a year's training, Minnie Midriffe increased her average speed in the London Marathon by 25%. By what percentage did her time decrease?

    A 50   B 30   C 20   D 10   E 5

17. The diagram shows three semicircles, each of radius one. What is the size of the total shaded area?

    A $\pi + 2$ B 5   C $\frac{3}{2}\pi + 1$
          D 4   E $2\pi - 1$

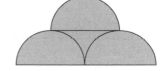

18. When dates are written using eight digits, e.g. 06 02 2003 for today, the 20th of February 2002 is a palindromic date since 20 02 2002 has the same digits in the same order when read in reverse. The previous palindromic date and the next few all occur in the month of February. What will be the next month other than February to have a palindromic date in it?

    A March   B April   C October   D November   E December

19. What is the area of the pentagon shown?

    A $\frac{1}{2}a(b - c)$ B $\frac{1}{2}b(a + c)$
    C $\frac{1}{2}a(b + c)$ D $\frac{1}{2}b(c - a)$
    E $\frac{1}{2}c(a + b)$

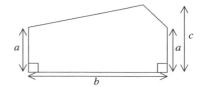

20. Suppose that e, i, n and t represent different positive whole numbers, $n + i + n + e = 9$, $t + e + n = 10$ and $i = 1$. What is t ?

A 2   B 3   C 4   D 5   E 6

21. In a leisure park there are three running tracks, all with the same Start and Finish, and all made from either one or two semicircles with centres on the same line.

Three runners P, Q and R start together at the Start and run at the same constant speed along the tracks as shown. In what order do they reach the Finish?

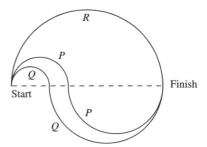

A P then Q then R B R first then P and Q together   C R then Q then P

D all three together   E more information needed

22. The diagram shows a regular dodecagon (a polygon with twelve equal sides and equal angles). What is the size of the marked angle?

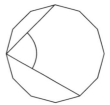

A   67.5°   B 72°   C 75°

D 82.5°   E 85°

23. Given that it takes a men b hours to paint c square metres of the Forth Bridge, how long would it take d men to paint e square metres of the bridge?

A $\dfrac{abe}{cd}$ B $\dfrac{abd}{ce}$ C $\dfrac{abc}{de}$ D $\dfrac{acd}{be}$ E $\dfrac{ace}{bd}$

24. The diagram shows a $1 \times x$ rectangular plank which fits neatly inside a 10×10 square frame. What is the value of x?

A $10 + 2\sqrt{2}$ B $10\sqrt{2} - 1$ C $10\sqrt{2} - 2$

D $10 + \sqrt{2}$ E 12

25. The width : height ratio of television screens is changing from the traditional 4 : 3 to the widescreen 16 : 9. If a traditional screen and a widescreen have the same area, then what is the ratio widescreen width : traditional width?

(Assume that television screens are rectangles.)

A 2 : $\sqrt{3}$ B 3 : 2   C 3 : $\sqrt{2}$ D 4 : 3   E none of these

Intermediate Challenge 2004

1. What is the value of 4002 − 2004?

   A 2004 B 2002 C 2000 D 1998 E 1996

2. You are told that 30 pupils have 25 different birthdays between them. What is the largest number of these pupils who could share the same birthday?

   A 2 B 3 C 4 D 5 E 6

3. Four of these numbers can make two pairs so that each pair adds up to 98 765. Which number is the odd one out?

   A 37 373 B 45 678 C 53 087 D 61 392 E 70 082

4. What is the value of $a + b + c + d + e + f$?

   A 360   B 540   C 720   D 900

   E it depends on the triangle

5. The sum of two numbers is 2. The difference between them is 4. What is their product?

   A −8 B −3 C 0 D 3 E 8

6. In Niatirb they use Cibara numerals. These are the same shape as normal Arabic numerals, but with the meanings in the opposite order. So "0" means "nine", "1" means "eight" and so on. But they write their numbers from left to right and use arithmetic symbols just as we do. So, for example, they use 62 for the number we write as 37.

   How do the inhabitants of Niatirb write the answer to the sum which they write as 837 + 742?

   A 419 B 580 C 1579 D 5317 E 8420

7. Which of the following straight lines cuts the shaded area in half?

   A *XA*   B *XB*   C *XC*   D *XD*   E *XE*

8. In March 2003 Welshman Tony Evans dropped a ball from an aircraft a mile above the Mojave desert to see if it would bounce. The ball was made from 6 million rubber bands, had a circumference of 14 ft 8 in, weighed 2600 pounds and took Mr Evans five years to build. On average, roughly how many rubber bands did he add each day whilst building the ball?

   A 3 B 33 C 330 D 3300 E 33 000

9. The cuboids below all have the same volume. Which of them has the greatest surface area?

   A   B   C   D   E

10. What is the mean of $\frac{1}{2}, \frac{1}{3}, \frac{1}{4}$ and $\frac{1}{6}$?

     A $\frac{1}{5}$ B $\frac{1}{15}$ C $\frac{5}{12}$ D $\frac{7}{24}$ E $\frac{5}{16}$

11. The diagram shows a square board in which strips of white squares alternate with strips of black and white squares. A larger board, constructed in the same way, has 49 black squares. How many white squares are there on the larger board?

     A 176   B 196   C 245   D 289   E 392

12. This figure is made from a straight line 16 cm long and two quarter circles, one with its centre at the midpoint of the straight line. What is the area of the figure (in cm^2)?

     A 64   B 16π C $32 + 16\pi$

     D 32π E $16 + 8\pi$

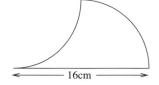

13. Four of these points lie on a single straight line. Which is the odd one out?

     A $(-3, -3)$ B $(-2, -1)$ C $(2, 5)$ D $(4, 11)$ E $(5, 13)$

14. In this addition sum, each letter represents a different non-zero digit. What is the value of $a + w + a + y$?

     A 13   B 15   C 16   D 17   E 18

$$\begin{array}{r} f\ l\ y \\ +\ f\ l\ y \\ +\ f\ l\ y \\ \hline a\ w\ a\ y \end{array}$$

15. Only one of these triangles can actually be made. Which is it?

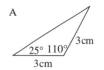

16. If the pattern shown is continued, what number will appear directly below 400?

     A 438   B 439   C 440   D 441   E 442

```
                 1
             2   3   4
         5   6   7   8   9
      10  11  12  13  14  15  16
```

17.

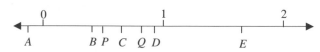

A, B, C, D, E, P and Q are points on the number line as shown. One of the points represents the product of the numbers represented by P and Q. Which is it?

     A   B   C   D   E

18. In the triangle PQR, there is a right angle at Q and angle QPR is 60°. The bisector of the angle QPR meets QR at S, as shown.

    What is the ratio $QS : SR$?

    A 1:1   B 1:√2   C 1:(3 − √3)   D 1 : √3   E 1:2

19. Three rectangular-shaped holes have been drilled passing all the way through a solid $3 \times 4 \times 5$ cuboid. The diagrams show the front, side and top views of the resulting block.

    What fraction of the original cuboid remains?

    A $\dfrac{13}{30}$ B $\dfrac{7}{15}$ C $\dfrac{1}{2}$ D $\dfrac{8}{15}$ E $\dfrac{17}{30}$

20. What is the largest power of 2 that divides $127^2 − 1$?

    A 2^1 B 2^7 C 2^8 D 2^{63} E 2^{127}

21. A square is divided into four congruent rectangles and a smaller square, as shown. (The diagram is not to scale.) The area of the small square is $\frac{1}{4}$ of the area of the whole square. What is the ratio of the length of a short side of one of the rectangles to the length of a long side?

    A 1:√2   B 1:√3   C 1:2   D 1:3   E 1:4

22. In a maths exam with N questions, you score m marks for a correct answer to each of the first q questions and $m + 2$ marks for a correct answer to each of the remaining questions. What is the maximum possible score?

    A $(m + 2)N − 2q$ B Nm C $mq + (m + 2)q$ D $N(m + 1)$ E $Nm + q(m + 2)$

23. In the diagram, the letter S is made from two arcs, KL and MN, which are each five-eighths of the circumference of a circle of radius 1, and the line segment LM, which is tangent to both circles. At points K and N, common tangents to the two circles touch one of the circles. What is the length LM?

    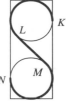

    A $\dfrac{3}{2}$ B $3 − \sqrt{2}$ C 2 D $\dfrac{3\sqrt{2}}{2}$ E $1 + \sqrt{2}$

24. If p, q and $p − q$ are all positive integers, which of the following is least?

    A $\dfrac{q^2}{p^2}$ B $\dfrac{p^2}{q^2}$ C $\dfrac{q}{p}$ D $\sqrt{\dfrac{q}{p}}$ E $\sqrt{\dfrac{p}{q}}$

25. The diagram shows a square with two lines from a corner to the middle of an opposite side. The rectangle fits exactly inside these two lines and the square itself. What fraction of the square is occupied by the shaded rectangle?

    A $\dfrac{1}{3}$ B $\dfrac{2}{5}$ C $\dfrac{3}{10}$ D $\dfrac{1}{2}$ E $\dfrac{3}{8}$

Intermediate Challenge 2005

1. If the following numbers are arranged in increasing order of size, which one is in the middle?

   A 4.04   B 4.004   C 4.4   D 4.44   E 4.044

2. What is the difference between 10% of one million and 10% of one thousand?

   A 9 900   B 9 990   C 90 900   D 99 900   E 999 900

3. Professor Rosseforp has an unusual clock. The clock shows the correct time at noon, but the hands move anti-clockwise rather than clockwise. The clock is very accurate, however, so the hands move at the correct speeds. If you looked in a mirror at the Professor's clock at 1:30 pm, which of the following would you see?

4. Which of the following expressions is equal to 2005?

   A $(1^2 + 1)(10^2 + 1)$ B $(2^2 + 1)(20^2 + 1)$ C $(3^2 + 1)(30^2 + 1)$
   D $(4^2 + 1)(40^2 + 1)$ E $(5^2 + 1)(50^2 + 1)$

5. How many of the statements in the box are true?

Any number which is divisible by 6 is even. Any number which is divisible by 9 is odd.
The sum of any two odd numbers is even.   The sum of any two even numbers is odd.

   A 0   B 1   C 2   D 3   E 4

6. A shop advertises 'Buy one, get one at half price'. For this offer, the average cost per item is the same as:

   A Two for the price of one   B Three for the price of one   C Three for the price of two
   D Four for the price of three   E Five for the price of four

7. In the diagram, what is the sum of the marked angles?

   A 180°   B 360°   C 450°   D 540°   E 720°

8. What fraction of a 24-hour day does school take up, if school starts at 8:30am and finishes at 3:15pm?

   A $\dfrac{9}{32}$ B $\dfrac{25}{96}$ C $\dfrac{13}{48}$ D $\dfrac{31}{96}$ E $\dfrac{18}{32}$

9. Which of the following shaded regions has an area different from the other shaded regions?

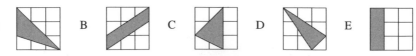

10. Granny has taken up deep-sea fishing! Last week, she caught a fish so big that she had to cut it into three pieces (head, body and tail) in order to weigh it. The tail weighed 9kg and the head weighed the same as the tail plus one third of the body. The body weighed as much as the head and tail together. How much did the whole fish weigh?

    A   18kg   B   27kg   C   54kg   D   77kg   E   84kg

11. If two of the sides of a right-angled triangle are 5 cm and 6 cm long, how many possibilities are there for the length of the third side?

    A   0   B   1   C   2   D   3   E   4

12. One gallon of honey provides enough fuel for a bee to fly about seven million miles. Roughly how many bees could fly one thousand miles if they had ten gallons of honey to share between them?

    A   7 000   B   70 000   C   700 000   D   7 000 000   E   70 000 000

13. The diagram shows two equilateral triangles. What is the value of x?

    A 70   B 60   C 50   D 40   E 30

14. Ten stones, of identical shape and size, are used to make an arch, as shown in the diagram. Each stone has a cross-section in the shape of a trapezium with three equal sides. What is the size of the smallest angles of the trapezium?

    A 72°   B 75°   C 81°   D 83°   E 85°

15. To make porridge, Goldilocks mixes together 3 bags of oats with 1 bag containing 20% wheat bran and 80% oats. All the bags have the same volume. What percentage of the volume of Goldilocks' porridge mixture is wheat bran?

    A   5%   B $6\frac{2}{3}$%   C   20%   D $26\frac{2}{3}$%   E   60%

16. A $1 \times 2 \times 3$ block is placed on an 8×8 board, as shown with the 1×2 face 'X' at the bottom. It is rolled over an edge without slipping onto the 1×3 face Y, then onto the 2×3 face Z, then onto X, Y, Z again in that order. How many different squares on the board has the block occupied altogether, including the starting and ending positions?

    A   18   B   19   C   20   D   21   E 22

17. Platinum is a very rare metal, even rarer <u>than</u> gold. Its density is 21.45 g/cm^3. Assuming that the world production has been about 110 tonnes for each of the past 50 years, and negligible before that, which of the following has a comparable volume to that of the total amount of platinum ever produced?

    A   a shoe box   B   a cupboard   C   a house
        D   Buckingham Palace   E   the Grand Canyon

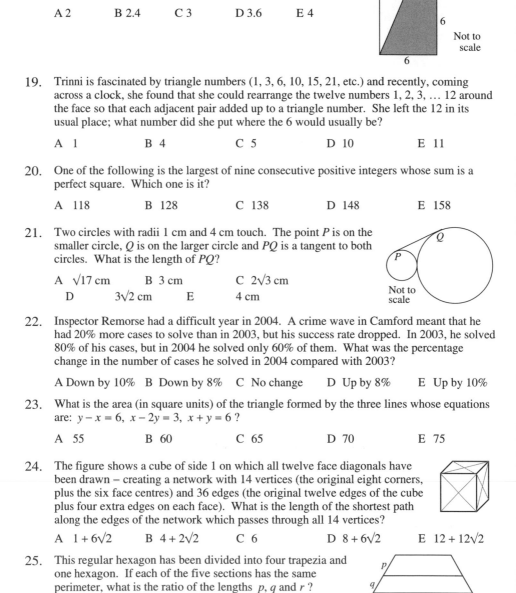

18. Three-quarters of the area of the rectangle has been shaded. What is the value of x?

    A 2   B 2.4   C 3   D 3.6   E 4

19. Trinni is fascinated by triangle numbers (1, 3, 6, 10, 15, 21, etc.) and recently, coming across a clock, she found that she could rearrange the twelve numbers 1, 2, 3, … 12 around the face so that each adjacent pair added up to a triangle number. She left the 12 in its usual place; what number did she put where the 6 would usually be?

    A 1   B 4   C 5   D 10   E 11

20. One of the following is the largest of nine consecutive positive integers whose sum is a perfect square. Which one is it?

    A 118   B 128   C 138   D 148   E 158

21. Two circles with radii 1 cm and 4 cm touch. The point P is on the smaller circle, Q is on the larger circle and PQ is a tangent to both circles. What is the length of PQ?

    A $\sqrt{17}$ cm   B 3 cm   C $2\sqrt{3}$ cm

    D $3\sqrt{2}$ cm   E   4 cm

22. Inspector Remorse had a difficult year in 2004. A crime wave in Camford meant that he had 20% more cases to solve than in 2003, but his success rate dropped. In 2003, he solved 80% of his cases, but in 2004 he solved only 60% of them. What was the percentage change in the number of cases he solved in 2004 compared with 2003?

    A Down by 10%   B Down by 8%   C No change   D Up by 8%   E Up by 10%

23. What is the area (in square units) of the triangle formed by the three lines whose equations are: $y - x = 6$, $x - 2y = 3$, $x + y = 6$?

    A 55   B 60   C 65   D 70   E 75

24. The figure shows a cube of side 1 on which all twelve face diagonals have been drawn – creating a network with 14 vertices (the original eight corners, plus the six face centres) and 36 edges (the original twelve edges of the cube plus four extra edges on each face). What is the length of the shortest path along the edges of the network which passes through all 14 vertices?

    A $1 + 6\sqrt{2}$ B $4 + 2\sqrt{2}$ C 6   D $8 + 6\sqrt{2}$ E $12 + 12\sqrt{2}$

25. This regular hexagon has been divided into four trapezia and one hexagon. If each of the five sections has the same perimeter, what is the ratio of the lengths p, q and r ?

    A $8 : 2 : 1$ B $12 : 4 : 1$ C $9 : 3 : 1$

    D $6 : 3 : 1$ E $9 : 4 : 1$

Intermediate Challenge 2006

1. What fraction is half-way between $\frac{1}{4}$ and $\frac{1}{6}$?

   A $\frac{1}{10}$ B $\frac{2}{9}$ C $\frac{5}{24}$ D $\frac{3}{14}$ E $\frac{7}{12}$

2. The diagram shows seven metal rings linked together. What is the smallest number of rings that need to be cut in order to separate all the rings?

   A 2 B 3 C 4 D 5 E 6

3. Which of the following is not prime?

   A $2^2 - 1$ B $2^3 - 1$ C $2^5 - 1$ D $2^6 - 1$ E $2^7 - 1$

4. The mean, median and mode of the numbers in the boxes below are the same. What is the missing number?

7	7	5	7	?

   A 6.5 B 7 C 8 D 8.5 E 9

5. A solid 'star' shape is created by gluing a square-based pyramid, in which each edge is of length 1 unit, precisely onto each face of a cube of edge 1 unit. How many faces does this 'star' have?

   A 18 B 24 C 30 D 36 E 48

6. Harriet Hare and Turbo Tortoise want to cross the finish line together on their 12 mile woodland race. Turbo sets off at 8:15 am and trots at a constant speed of 4 mph. Given that Harriet runs at a constant speed of 8 mph, at what time should she set off?

   A 9:45 am B 10:15 am C 10:45 am D 11:15 am E 11:45 pm

7. The Queen of Spades always lies for the whole day or always tells the truth for the whole day. Which of these statements can she never say?

   A "Yesterday, I told the truth." B "Yesterday, I lied." C "Today, I tell the truth."
   D "Today, I lie." E "Tomorrow, I shall tell the truth."

8. Sydney flew to Melbourne, Australia. The flying time to Melbourne, which is 11 hours ahead of Britain, was 21 hours. Sydney's flight left London at 11.30am on Tuesday. What time was it in Melbourne when Sydney's flight arrived?

   A 9:30pm on Tuesday B 8:30am on Wednesday C 7:30pm on Wednesday
   D 6:30am on Thursday E 7:30pm on Thursday

9. The diagram shows 10 identical coins which fit exactly inside a wooden frame. As a result each coin is prevented from sliding. What is the largest number of coins that may be removed so that each remaining coin is still unable to slide?

   A 1 B 2 C 3 D 4 E 5

10. Gill is 18 this year. She and I went to a restaurant for lunch to celebrate her birthday. The bill for lunch for the two of us came to £25.50. Gill paid the bill by credit card and I left a £2.50 tip in cash. We agreed to split the total cost equally. How much did I owe Gill?

    A £11   B £11.50   C £12   D £12.50   E £13

11. What is the obtuse angle between the hands of a clock at 6 minutes past 8 o'clock?

    A 123°   B 126°   C 153°   D 156°   E 159°

12. When a solid cube is held up to the light, how many of the following shapes could its shadow have?

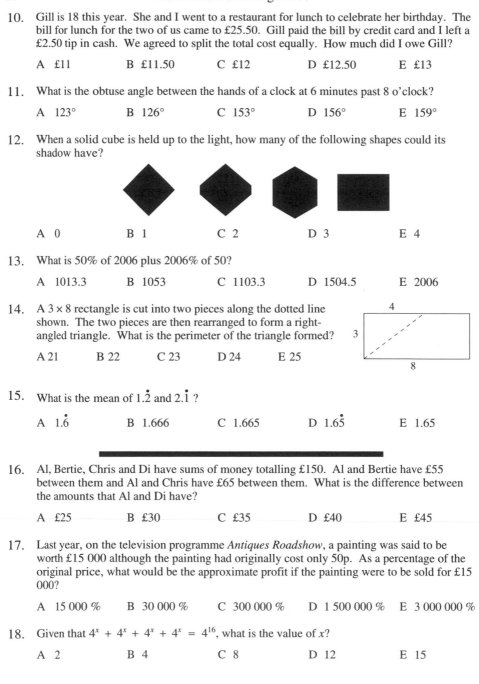

    A 0   B 1   C 2   D 3   E 4

13. What is 50% of 2006 plus 2006% of 50?

    A 1013.3   B 1053   C 1103.3   D 1504.5   E 2006

14. A 3×8 rectangle is cut into two pieces along the dotted line shown. The two pieces are then rearranged to form a right-angled triangle. What is the perimeter of the triangle formed?

    A 21   B 22   C 23   D 24   E 25

15. What is the mean of $1.\dot{2}$ and $2.\dot{1}$?

    A $1.\dot{6}$ B 1.666   C 1.665   D $1.6\dot{5}$ E 1.65

16. Al, Bertie, Chris and Di have sums of money totalling £150. Al and Bertie have £55 between them and Al and Chris have £65 between them. What is the difference between the amounts that Al and Di have?

    A £25   B £30   C £35   D £40   E £45

17. Last year, on the television programme *Antiques Roadshow*, a painting was said to be worth £15 000 although the painting had originally cost only 50p. As a percentage of the original price, what would be the approximate profit if the painting were to be sold for £15 000?

    A 15 000 %   B 30 000 %   C 300 000 %   D 1 500 000 %   E 3 000 000 %

18. Given that $4^x + 4^x + 4^x + 4^x = 4^{16}$, what is the value of x?

    A 2   B 4   C 8   D 12   E 15

19. The diagram shows a regular pentagon and a regular hexagon which overlap. What is the value of x ?

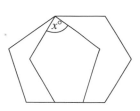

A 82   B 84   C 85   D 87   E 91

20. Given that the number 2006 is the correct answer to the calculation

$$1 - 2 + 3 - 4 + 5 - 6 + \ldots + (n - 2) - (n - 1) + n,$$

what is the sum of the digits of n ?

A 3   B 4   C 5   D 6   E 7

21. The diagram shows two semicircular arcs, $PQRS$ and QOR. The diameters, PS and QR, of the two semicircles are parallel; PS is of length 4 and is a tangent to semicircular arc QOR.

What is the area of the shaded region?

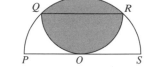

A $2\pi - 2$ B 3π C π D   4 E $2\pi - 4$

22. An 8 by 8 chessboard is placed so that a black square is in the top left-hand corner. Starting in the top left square and working along each row in turn, coloured counters are placed, one on each square, following the sequence black, white, red, black, white, red and so on. When the right-hand end of each row is reached, the pattern continues, starting at the left-hand end of the row beneath, until there is one counter on every square.

In the final arrangement, what fraction of the counters are on squares of the same colour as themselves?

A $\dfrac{11}{32}$ B $\dfrac{23}{64}$ C $\dfrac{7}{16}$ D $\dfrac{1}{2}$ E $\dfrac{2}{3}$

23. In the figure on the right, $PQ = 2\frac{1}{3}$, $PS = 6\frac{6}{7}$ and $\angle QPR = \angle RPS$.
How long is PR?

A $3\frac{1}{2}$ B 4   C $4\frac{1}{4}$ D $4\frac{25}{42}$ E 5

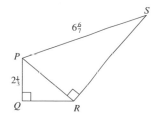

24. The diagram shows a square of area x square units inscribed inside a semicircle and a larger square of area y square units inscribed inside a circle.

What is the ratio $x : y$?

A $1 : \sqrt{2}$ B $1 : 2$ C $2 : 5$ D $1 : 3$ E $\sqrt{3} : 4$

25. Given that $5^j + 6^k + 7^l + 11^m = 2006$ where j, k, l and m are different non-negative integers, what is the value of $j + k + l + m$?

A 6   B 7   C 8   D 9   E 10

Senior Challenge 1997

1. Which of these calculations does not give the same answer as the rest?

   A $2 + 4 \times 2$ B $(-24) \div (-2)$ C $-3 - (-15)$ D $24 \times (0.5)$ E $(-7) + 19$

2. The average of five consecutive integers is 10. What is the sum of the second and fourth of these integers?

   A 6   B 10   C 20   D 21   E can't be sure

3. A rhombus has diagonals of lengths 2cm and 3cm. What is its area (in cm^2)?

   A 2   B 3   C 4   D 5   E 6

4. Timmy Riddle was selling toffee apples at the school fête. When I asked him what they cost he said "One toffee apple costs the smallest amount that cannot be paid exactly using four or fewer standard British coins".
   I bought as many toffee apples as I could get for £1. How much change did I receive?

   A 1p   B 5p   C 18p   D 22p   E 24p

5. Eight unit cubes are arranged to form an imaginary 2 by 2 by 2 cube. What is the largest number of unit cubes one can remove from this arrangement if the resulting shape has to have the same surface area as the original?

   A 0   B 1   C 2   D 3   E 4

6. Here are the measurements of five different rectangles. The list includes two pairs of *similar* rectangles, while one rectangle differs in shape from all the others. Which is the odd one out?

   A 240×120 B 300×180 C 55×110 D 320×200 E 210×350

7. The first six volumes of the *Encyclopedia of Mathematicians* are arranged in order on my shelf from left to right. The six volumes contain names beginning A-Ba, Be-Ca, Ce-Ei, Ek-Fe, Fee-Fi, Fo-Fum. If one ignores the covers, which of the following encyclopedia entries could be on a page "next to" the page with the entry for Einstein?

   A Abel   B Bernoulli   C Cantor   D Euler   E Fibonacci

8. A teacher gave a test to 20 students. Marks on the test ranged from 0 to 10 inclusive. The average of the first twelve papers marked was 6.5. What can you conclude from this about the eventual average M for the whole group?

   A $0.325 \leqslant M \leqslant 6.5$ B $3.25 \leqslant M \leqslant 6.5$ C $3.9 \leqslant M \leqslant 6.5$
           D $3.9 \leqslant M \leqslant 7.9$ E $6.5 \leqslant M \leqslant 7.9$

9. A cube $ABCDEFGH$ has $ABCD$ as square base, with E, F, G, H above A, B, C, D respectively. What is the cosine of the angle $\angle CAG$?

   A $1/\sqrt{3}$ B $\sqrt{2}/3$ C $1/\sqrt{2}$ D $\sqrt{(2/3)}$ E $\sqrt{3}/2$

10. If n is some integer, $1 \leqslant n \leqslant 9$, what is the value of $(0.n)/(0.\dot{n})$?

    A $1/10$ B $9/10$ C 1   D $10/9$ E it depends on n

11. Which of these five expressions represents the largest number?

    A $9^{(9^9)}$ B 999 C 9^{99} D $(9^9)^9$ E 99^9

12. What is the value of

    $1 + 2(1 + 2(1 + 2(1 + 2(1 + 2(1 + 2(1 + 2(1 + 2(1 + 2(1 + 2))))))))))$?

    A $2^{10} + 1$ B $2^{11} - 1$ C $2^{11} + 1$ D $2^{12} - 1$ E $2^{12} + 1$

13. Last year Noel bought a number of identically priced Christmas cards. The total cost was £15.60. In a gesture of seasonal goodwill the shopkeeper gave him one extra card free, and this reduced the average cost per card by exactly 1p. At their original price how many cards could Noel have bought with £5?

    A 8   B 12   C 16   D 20   E 24

14. I am trying to do a rectangular jigsaw puzzle. The puzzle was made by starting with a rectangular picture and then cutting it into 1000 pieces by sawing along the lines of a (wiggly!) rectangular grid. I start by separating out all the edge and corner pieces. Which of the following could *not* possibly be the number of corner and edge pieces of such a jigsaw?

    A 126   B 136   C 216   D 316   E A-D are all possible

15. Triangle ABC is isosceles with $AB = AC$, and D is the midpoint of AB.
    If $\angle BCD = \angle BAC = \theta$, then $\cos \theta$ equals

    A 3/4   B $\sqrt{7}/(2\sqrt{2})$ C $1/\sqrt{2}$ D $\sqrt{7}/4$ E $1/(2\sqrt{2})$

16. AA' and BB' are arcs of concentric circles with centre O and with radii a and b respectively. Let $\angle A'OA = x°$. The length of the arc AA' is equal to the total distance from A to A' via the arc BB'. Find the value of x to the nearest integer.

    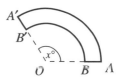

    A 115   B 120   C 125   D 135   E it depends on a and b

17. For each real number x, except $x = 0, 1, -1$, let $f(x) = \dfrac{(x \quad 1)}{(x + 1)}$.
    Then $f^6(x) = f(f(f(f(f(f(x))))))$ equals

    A $\dfrac{(x+1)}{(x-1)}$ B $\dfrac{-1}{x}$ C x D $\dfrac{1}{x}$ E $\left[\dfrac{x-1}{x+1}\right]$

18. Which of the following equations could be the equation of the "curve", part of which is shown on the right?

    A $y = \sin x$ B $|y| = \sin x$ C $y = |\sin x|$ D $|y| = |\sin x|$ E A-D all impossible

19. One end of an egg-timer is a hemisphere of radius r; the other end is
     a cone of radius r and height r. Both ends are attached to cylinders
     of radius r. When the hemisphere is at the bottom, the sand in the
     egg-timer comes to a height $2r$ above the lowest point. What is the
     corresponding height of the sand when the egg-timer has been turned
     over and all the sand has been allowed to run through to the other
     end?

     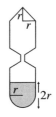

     A $\frac{4}{3}r$ B $\frac{5}{3}r$ C $2r$ D $(\frac{1}{2} + \frac{\pi}{4})r$ E $\frac{7}{3}r$

20. In a triangle the perpendicular from a vertex to the opposite side is called an *altitude*. If h,
     h', h'' denote the lengths of the three altitudes of a triangle, which of the following ratios
     never occurs as the ratio $h : h' : h''$?
     A $2:3:4$ B $2:3:5$ C $2:4:5$ D $3:4:5$ E $3:4:6$

21. A square is divided into nine rectangles by two horizontal and two
     vertical lines. The areas of three of the small rectangles are as shown.

     If the central small rectangle happens to be a square, what is the
     perimeter of the small rectangle in the bottom left corner?

     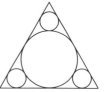

     A $2/\sqrt{3}$ B 2 C $3\sqrt{3}$ D 6 E $11/\sqrt{3}$

22. Which of the following expressions is identically equal to $\sin^3 x + \cos^3 x$?
     A $\sin 3x + \cos 3x$ B 1 C $(\sin x + \cos x)(1 - \sin x \cos x)$
              D $(\sin x + \cos x)^3$ E $(\sin x + \cos x)(2 \sin x \cos x + 1)$

23. A circle is inscribed in an equilateral triangle. Small circles are
     then inscribed in each corner as shown. What is the ratio of the area
     of a small circle to that of the large circle?

     A $1:3$ B $1:4.5$ C $1:3\sqrt{3}$ D $1:6$ E $1:9$

24. The curvy shape ABC shown here is called a *Reuleaux* triangle
     (after the French engineer *Franz Reuleaux* (1829- 1905)). Its
     perimeter consists of three equal arcs AB, BC, CA each with the
     same radius and centred at the opposite vertex. In the *Reuleaux*
     triangle shown, each arc has radius 3cm. What is the area (in
     cm^2) of the inscribed circle?

     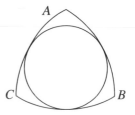

     A $6\pi(2 - \sqrt{3})$ B $9\pi/4$ C $2\pi(3 - \sqrt{3})$ D $3\pi/4$ E 9π

25. A right circular cone has apex angle 2α. A sphere is inscribed in the cone, touching the
     base. What fraction of the cone is occupied by the sphere?
     A $2 \sin \alpha \cos 2\alpha/(1 + \cos \alpha)^3$ B $4 \sin \alpha (1 - \sin \alpha)/ \cos^2 \alpha$ C $4(1 - \sin \alpha)^3 \sin \alpha/ \cos^4 \alpha$
              D $\sin 2\alpha \cos \alpha/(1 + \sin \alpha)^3$ E need more information

Senior Challenge 1998

1. The sum of five consecutive even numbers is 60. What is the smallest of the five numbers?

   A 8 　　　　 B 10 　　　　 C 12 　　　　 D 14 　　　　 E 16

2. In a class of thirty pupils, there are twenty-two pupils who are right-handed and there are fourteen girls. What is the smallest number of girls who could be right-handed?

   A 0 　　　　 B 2 　　　　 C 4 　　　　 D 6 　　　　 E 8

3. The *integer part* of a positive number is the part before the decimal point; the *decimal part* is the part after the decimal point. For example, the integer part of 3.72 is '3' and the decimal part is '0.72'. Which of the following numbers has decimal part equal to exactly one eighth of the integer part?

   A 0.05 　　　　 B 1.15 　　　　 C 2.25 　　　　 D 3.35 　　　　 E 4.45

4. The smaller circle touches the larger circle, and goes through the centre of the larger circle. What fraction of the area of the larger circle is outside the smaller circle?

   A $\frac{2}{3}$ 　　　 B $\frac{3}{4}$ 　　　 C $\frac{4}{5}$ 　　　 D $\frac{5}{6}$ 　　　 E $\frac{7}{8}$

5. A square has the same perimeter as a 4cm by 2cm rectangle. What is the area of the square (in cm^2)?

   A 4 　　　　 B 8 　　　　 C 9 　　　　 D 10 　　　　 E 12

6. Observe that $18 = 4^2 + 1^2 + 1^2 + 0^2$. How many of the first fifteen positive integers can be written as the sum of the squares of four integers?

   A 11 　　　　 B 12 　　　　 C 13 　　　　 D 14 　　　　 E 15

7. Mary's height increased by 30% between her 5th birthday and her 10th birthday. It increased by 20% between her 10th birthday and her 15th birthday. By how much did her height increase between her 5th birthday and her 15th birthday?

   A 50% 　　　　 B 52% 　　　　 C 54% 　　　　 D 56% 　　　　 E 60%

8. When the following five numbers are arranged in numerical order, which one is in the middle?

   A $4\sqrt{15}$ 　　　 B $5\sqrt{10}$ 　　　 C $7\sqrt{5}$ 　　　 D $9\sqrt{3}$ 　　　 E $11\sqrt{2}$

9. Pascal, Newton, Galileo and Fermat all took the same test. The average score of all four candidates was 16; Pascal and Newton had an average of 16, Pascal and Fermat had an average of 13, while Newton and Fermat had an average of 18. What was Galileo's score?

   A 14 　　　　 B 15 　　　　 C 16 　　　　 D 17 　　　　 E 18

10. Roughly how many seconds are there in a day?

    A 10^3 　　　 B 10^4 　　　 C 10^5 　　　 D 10^6 　　　 E 10^7

11. Note that 1647/8235 = 1/5. Start with 1647/8235. First delete one digit from the numerator and one digit from the denominator leaving a fraction A/B which is equivalent to the fraction you started with. Then delete one digit from the new numerator A and one digit from the new denominator B leaving a fraction C/D which is equivalent to A/B. What is the value of the difference $D - C$?

A 64   B 68   C 72   D 76   E 80

12. *ABCDEFGH* is a regular octagon. P is the point inside the octagon such that triangle *ABP* is equilateral. What is the size of angle *APC*?

A 90°   B 112.5°   C 117.5°   D 120°   E 135°

13. If $x = (1/4)^{1/2}$, what is the value of x^{-x}?

A 1/4   B 1/2   C $1/\sqrt{2}$ D $\sqrt{2}$ E 2

14. The smaller circle has radius 10 units; *AB* is a diameter. The larger circle has centre A, radius 12 units and cuts the smaller circle at C. What is the length of the chord *CB*?

A 8   B 10   C 12   D $10\sqrt{2}$ E 16

15. A jogger runs a certain distance at V ms^{-1}, and then walks half that distance at U ms^{-1}. If the total time for the two stages is T seconds, what is the total distance travelled (in metres)?

A $\dfrac{3TUV}{U + 2V}$ B $\dfrac{3TUV}{2U + V}$ C $\dfrac{3T}{U + 2V}$ D $\dfrac{TUV}{2U + V}$ E $\dfrac{2TUV}{2U + V}$

16. The probability of a single ticket winning the jackpot in the National Lottery is

$$\frac{6}{49} \times \frac{5}{48} \times \frac{4}{47} \times \frac{3}{46} \times \frac{2}{45} \times \frac{1}{44}.$$

If I buy one ticket every week, approximately how often might I expect to win the jackpot?

A once every hundred years   B once every twenty thousand years

C once every hundred thousand years   D once every quarter of a million years

E once every million years

17. $(x - 1)(x^4 + 1)(x^2 + 1)(x + 1)$ equals

A $x^8 - 1$ B $x^8 + x^6 + x^4 + x^2 + 1$ C $x^8 + 1$

D $x^8 + x^7 + x^6 + x^5 + x^4 + x^3 + x^2 + x + 1$ E $x^8 - x^6 + x^4 - 1$

18. A cylindrical hole of radius r and of length $4r$ is bored symmetrically through a solid cylinder of radius $2r$ and length $4r$. What is the total surface area of the resulting solid?

A $22\pi r^2$ B $24\pi r^2$ C $28\pi r^2$ D $30\pi r^2$ E $36\pi r^2$

19. If $\cos\theta = 1/2$, which of these cannot equal $\sin 2\theta$?

A $\sin\theta$ B $1/2$ C $-\sqrt{3}/2$ D $\sqrt{3}/2$ E $2\cos\theta\sin\theta$

20. A cube is inscribed in a sphere of diameter 1m. What is the surface area of the cube?

     A 2 m^2 B 3 m^2 C 4 m^2 D 5 m^2 E 6 m^2

21. The expression "$3 \oplus 7 \rightarrow 4$" is a short way of writing the statement "it is possible to fit a 3-sided polygon and a 7-sided polygon together (without overlap) and so make a 4-sided polygon". This statement is correct (as shown in the diagram on the right). Which of the following represents a statement which is *not* correct?

     A $3 \oplus 5 \rightarrow 4$ B $3 \oplus 6 \rightarrow 4$ C $3 \oplus 8 \rightarrow 4$ D $4 \oplus 6 \rightarrow 4$ E $4 \oplus 8 \rightarrow 4$

22. Triangle ABC has $A\hat{B}C = 90°$ and $A\hat{C}B = 30°$. If a point inside the triangle is chosen at random, what is the probability that it is nearer to AB than it is to AC?

     A $\dfrac{\sqrt{3}}{2}$ B $\dfrac{1}{2}$ C $\dfrac{1}{\sqrt{3}}$ D $\dfrac{1}{3}$ E $\dfrac{1}{4}$

23. Circles with radii r and R (where $r < R$) touch each other and also touch two perpendicular lines as shown. What is the value of R/r?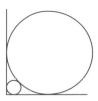

     A $5 + \sqrt{2}$ B 5.75 C $\sqrt{40}$

         D 6 E $3 + 2\sqrt{2}$

24. If $x^2 - 3x + 1 = 0$, what is the value of $x^2 + (1/x)^2$?

     A 7 B $(7 - 3\sqrt{5})/2$ C 9 D $(7 + 3\sqrt{5})/2$ E 10

25. A company logo has a centrally-symmetric white cross of width $\sqrt{2}$ on a dark circle. The dark corner pieces have sides of length 1 as indicated. What is the total area of the corners?

     A $\pi(2 - \sqrt{2}) + \dfrac{\sqrt{2}}{2}$ B $\pi - \dfrac{1}{\sqrt{2}}$ C $\pi(4 - \sqrt{2}) - 4\sqrt{2}$

         D $\dfrac{(\pi + \sqrt{2})}{2}$ E $\dfrac{\pi(2 + \sqrt{2})}{2} - 2\sqrt{2}$

Senior Challenge 1999

1. How many prime numbers are there less than 20?

   A 6   B 7   C 8   D 9   E 10

2. What is the largest number of Sundays that there can be in any one year?

   A 50   B 51   C 52   D 53   E 54

3. Which of the following is not the net of a pyramid?

   A   B   C   D   E

4. I need to buy 12 films for my camera before my holiday. They normally cost £4.50 each, but a number of shops have "special offers". Which of these is the best deal?

   A One fifth off all prices!   B Two for the price of four!   C Buy two – get one free!

   D 30% price cut!   E Pay only three quarters of the normal price!

5. In 1998 a newspaper reported that "The world record for remembering the value of π to the greatest number of decimal places is 40 000 places, which took the record holder 17 hours and 21 minutes to recite."

   What was the average number of decimal places recited per minute, approximately?

   A 20   B 40   C 200   D 400   E 2000

6. Our ancient Ancient History teacher's copy of Homer's *Odyssey* cost 40p in 1974. A similar edition today costs £5. What percentage increase is this?

   A 12.5%   B 1150%   C 1250%   D 12400%   E 12500%

7. The size of each exterior angle of a regular polygon is one quarter of the size of an interior angle. How many sides does the polygon have?

   A 6   B 8   C 9   D 10   E 12

8. Two numbers differ by 9 and have sum 99. What is the ratio of the larger number to the smaller?

   A 5:4   B 6:5   C 7:6   D 8:7   E 9:8

9. The factorial of n, written $n!$, is defined by $n! = 1 \times 2 \times 3 \times \ldots \times (n-2) \times (n-1) \times n$

   e.g. $6! = 1 \times 2 \times 3 \times 4 \times 5 \times 6 = 720$.

   What is the smallest positive integer which is *not* a factor of 50! ?

   A 51   B 52   C 53   D 54   E 55

10. Which is the largest of the following?

    A $\sqrt{1999}$ B $1\sqrt{999}$ C $19\sqrt{99}$ D $199\sqrt{9}$ E $1999\sqrt{0}$

11. In how many different ways can I circle letters in the grid shown so that there is exactly one circled letter in each row and exactly one circled letter in each column?

A	B	C	D	E
F	G	H	I	J
K	L	M	N	O
P	Q	R	S	T
U	V	W	X	Y

    A 15   B 24   C 60   D 100   E 120

12. Earlier this year, the White Rabbit said to me, "Two days ago, Alice was still thirteen, but her sixteenth birthday will be next year." When is Alice's birthday?

    A Jan 1st   B Feb 28th   C Feb 29th   D Dec 30th   E Dec 31st

13. Two square pieces of card, each 3 cm × 3 cm, are attached by a single pin to a board. The pin passes through a point 1/3 of the way along the diagonal of each square and the squares overlap exactly. The bottom card now remains fixed, while the top card is rotated through 180°. What is the area of overlap of the cards in this new position?

    A 1 cm^2 B 2 cm^2 C 4 cm^2 D 6 cm^2 E 9 cm^2

14. The line whose equation is $y = 3x + 4$ is reflected in the line whose equation is $y = -x$. What is the equation of the image line?

    A $3y = x + 4$ B $3y = x - 4$ C $y = 3x - 4$ D $y = -3x - 4$ E $y = 4x + 3$

15. Three people each think of a number which is the product of two different primes. Which of the following could be the product of the three numbers which are thought of?

    A 120   B 144   C 240   D 3000   E 12100

16. When rounded to 3 significant figures, the number x is written as 1000. What is the largest range of possible values of x?

    A $999 \leqslant x < 1001$ B $995 \leqslant x < 1005$ C $990 \leqslant x < 1010$
    D $999.5 \leqslant x < 1005$ E $999.5 \leqslant x < 1000.5$

17. The ratio of Jon's age to Jan's age is 3 : 1. Three years ago the ratio was 4 : 1. In how many years time will the ratio be 2 : 1?

    A 3   B 6   C 9   D 12   E 15

18. The diagram shows two concentric circles. The chord of the large circle is a tangent to the small circle and has length $2p$. What is the area of the shaded region?

    A πp^2 B $2\pi p^2$ C $3\pi p^2$ D $4\pi p^2$
    E more information needed

19. P is a vertex of a cuboid and Q, R and S are three points on the edges as shown. $PQ = 2$ cm, $PR = 2$ cm and $PS = 1$ cm. What is the area, in cm^2, of triangle QRS?

    A $\sqrt{15}/4$ B 5/2   C $\sqrt{6}$ D $2\sqrt{2}$ E $\sqrt{10}$

20. What is the 1999th term of the sequence 1, 2, 2, 3, 3, 3, 4, 4, 4, 4, 5, ... ?

  A 59   B 60   C 61   D 62   E 63

21. Just one of the following is a prime number. Which one is it?

  A $1000^2 + 111^2$ B $555^2 + 666^2$ C $2000^2 - 999^2$
  D $1001^2 + 1002^2$ E $1001^2 + 1003^2$

22.

 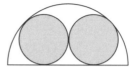

The area of each large semicircle is 2. What is the difference between the black and grey shaded areas?

  A 0   B $\dfrac{1}{2}$ C $1 + 2\sqrt{2}$ D $\dfrac{5}{9}$ E $23 - 16\sqrt{2}$

23. The statement "There are exactly four integer values of n for which $(2n + y)/(n - 2)$ is itself an integer" is true for certain values of y only. For how many values of y in the range $1 \leqslant y \leqslant 20$ is the statement true?

  A 0   B 7   C 8   D 10   E 20

24. The figure shows a hexagon $AZBXCY$ made from four congruent tiles. The shape and position of the tiles are given by triangle ABC and the three reflections of triangle ABC in the lines determined by its sides. For example, ABZ is the image of ABC when reflected in the line determined by AB. If a polygon is made from five tiles whose shape and position are determined by a quadrilateral and the four reflections of that quadrilateral in the lines determined by its sides, what is the smallest possible number of sides of the resulting polygon?

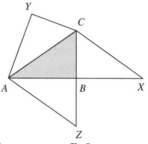

  A 4   B 5   C 6   D 7   E 8

25. What is the sum to infinity of the convergent series

$$\frac{1}{2} + \frac{1}{4} + \frac{2}{8} + \frac{3}{16} + \frac{5}{32} + \frac{8}{64} + \frac{13}{128} + \frac{21}{256} + \frac{34}{512} + \ ... \ ?$$

  A $\dfrac{7}{4}$ B 2   C $\sqrt{5}$ D $\dfrac{9}{4}$ E $\dfrac{7}{3}$

Senior Challenge 2000

1. What is the remainder when the number 743589×301647 is divided by 5?

   A 0   B 1   C 2   D 3   E 4

2. When written in decimal form, $\dfrac{1}{81} = 0.0123456790123....$ What is the value of $\dfrac{2}{81}$ correct to six decimal places?

   A 0.02468   B 0.024681   C 0.024690   D 0.024691   E 0.0246914

3. Annakin Skywalker and Obi-Wan Kenobi each has some coins in his pocket. If Annakin gave Obi-Wan Kenobi one coin then Obi-Wan Kenobi would have twice as many coins as Annakin, but if Obi-Wan Kenobi gave Annakin one coin, they would each have the same number of coins. Altogether, how many coins do they have?

   A 8   B 10   C 12   D 14   E 16

4. An attempt by two men to sit in every one of the 72 000 seats in Cardiff's Millennium Stadium to raise money for charity ended in painful failure, despite their wearing man-made-fibre tracksuits to help them slide from seat to seat. Before the pain stopped them, they had managed 64 000 seats between them in 27 hours. On average, roughly how long did each man take per seat?

   A 0.5 seconds   B 1 second   C 1.5 seconds   D 2 seconds   E 3 seconds

5. *ABCD* is a rectangle. *P* is the midpoint of *AD*; the length of *BQ* is one third of the length of *BC*. What fraction of the area of the rectangle is the area of the shaded quadrilateral *ABQP*?

   A $\dfrac{5}{12}$ B $\dfrac{2}{5}$ C $\dfrac{3}{8}$ D $\dfrac{1}{3}$ E $\dfrac{7}{16}$

6. Last year, a newspaper reported that the mean forecourt price of petrol was 73.3 pence per litre for unleaded petrol. The price before tax, however, was 15.2 pence per litre. What was the approximate percentage increase from the price before tax to the mean forecourt price?

   A 20%   B 40%   C 80%   D 400%   E 500%

7. The three regular hexagons are all the same size. *X*, *Y* and *Z* denote the values of the shaded areas in the hexagons, as shown.

   Which of the following statements is true?
   A *X* is equal to *Y* but not to *Z*   B *X* is equal to *Z*, but not to *Y*
   C *Y* is equal to *Z*, but not to *X*   D *X* is equal to *Y* and to *Z*
   E *X*, *Y* and *Z* are all different

8. A van travels from Newcastle to South Shields at an average speed of 30 mph and returns by the same route at an average speed of 40 mph. Which of the following is closest to the van's average speed for the whole journey?

   A 33 mph   B 34 mph   C 35.5 mph   D 36 mph   E more information needed

9. What is the value of $\left(61^2 - 39^2\right) \div \left(51^2 - 49^2\right)$?

    A 10·5   B 11   C 12   D 21   E 22

10. A square piece of wood, of side 8 cm, is painted black and fixed to a table. An equal square, painted white, is placed on the table alongside the black square and has a point P marked one quarter of the way along a diagonal, as shown. Whilst keeping the same orientation on the table and always remaining in contact with the black square, the white square now slides once around the black square. Through what distance does P move?

    A 32 cm   B 48 cm   C 64 cm   D 72 cm   E 80 cm

11. Given that a and b are integers greater than zero, which of the following equations could be true?

    A $a - b = a \div b$ B $a + b = a \div b$ C $a - b = a \times b$

          D $a + b = a - b$ E $\sqrt{a + b} = \sqrt{a} + \sqrt{b}$

12. Observe that $2000 = 2^4 \times 5^3$. What is the number of the next year after the year 2000 which can be written $a^b \times c^d$ where a, b, c, d are 2, 3, 4, 5 in some order?

    A 2016   B 2025   C 2040   D 2048   E 2050

13. A trapezium has parallel sides of length a and b, and height h. Sides a and b are both decreased by 10% and the height h is increased by 10%.

    What is the percentage change in the area of the trapezium?

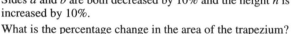

    A 10% decrease   B 1% decrease   C no change

          D 10% increase   E 30% increase

14. Which shape cannot be obtained as the cross-section (in any direction) of this solid, which is a triangular prism with three rectangular faces?

    A triangle   B rectangle   C trapezium   D pentagon   E hexagon

15. The diagram represents the addition of three 3-digit numbers, which between them use all the digits from 1 to 9. Which of the following cannot be obtained as the answer to the addition?

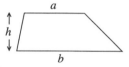

    A 1500   B 1503   C 1512   D 1521   E 1539

16. A roll of adhesive tape is wound round a central cylindrical core of radius 3 cm. The outer radius of a roll containing 20 m of tape is 4 cm. Approximately, what is the outer radius of a roll containing 80 m of tape?

    A 5 cm   B 5·5 cm   C 6 cm   D 7 cm   E 12 cm

17. The following equation is true for all a, b and c:
$$a^3 + b^3 + c^3 = (a + b + c)^3 - 3(a + b + c)(ab + bc + ca) + kabc$$
What is the value of k?

    A −6   B −3   C 0   D 3   E 6

18. The curve $y = x^2 - 6x + 11$ is rotated through $180°$ about the origin. What is the equation of the new curve?

A $y = x^2 + 6x + 11$ B $y = x^2 - 6x - 11$ C $y = -x^2 + 6x - 11$

     D $y = -x^2 - 6x + 11$ E $y = -x^2 - 6x - 11$

19. In the diagram, O is the centre of the circle, $\angle AOB = \alpha$ and $\angle COD = \beta$. What is the size of $\angle AXB$ in terms of α and β?

A $\frac{1}{2}\alpha - \frac{1}{2}\beta$ B $90° - \frac{1}{2}\alpha - \frac{1}{2}\beta$ C $\alpha - \beta$

D $180° - \alpha - \beta$ E   more information needed

20. What is the maximum possible value of the product of a list of positive integers, which are not necessarily all different, given that the sum of these numbers is 100?

A 10^{10} B 2^{50} C $2^{20} \times 3^{20}$ D 5^{20} E $2^2 \times 3^{32}$

21. What is the radius of the shaded semicircle?

A $\sqrt{2} - 1$ B $\dfrac{1}{\sqrt{2}}$ C $3 - 2\sqrt{2}$ D $\dfrac{1}{2}$ E $2 - \sqrt{2}$

22. Given that $0 < b < a$ and $a^2 + b^2 - 6ab$, what is the value of $\dfrac{a + b}{a - b}$?

A $\dfrac{1}{\sqrt{2}}$ B $\sqrt{2}$ C $\dfrac{1}{\sqrt{2} - 1}$ D $2\sqrt{2}$ E $\sqrt{6}$

23. A tennis club has n left-handed players and $2n$ right-handed players, but in total there are fewer than 20 players. At last summer's tournament, in which every player in the club played every other player exactly once, no matches were drawn and the ratio of the number of matches won by left-handed players to the number of matches won by right-handed players was 3 : 4.

What is the value of n?

A   3   B   4   C   5   D   6   E   more information needed

24. How many pairs of positive integers (x, y) satisfy the equation $\sqrt{x} - \sqrt{17} = \sqrt{y}$?

A   0   B   1   C   2   D   17   E   infinitely many

25. The figure on the right shows two parallel lines, ℓ_1, and ℓ_2. Line ℓ_1 is a tangent to circles C_1 and C_3, line ℓ_2 is a tangent to circles C_2 and C_3 and the three circles touch as shown. Circles C_1 and C_2 have radius s and t respectively.

What is the radius of circle C_3?

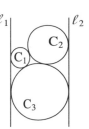

A $2\sqrt{s^2 + t^2}$ B $s + t$ C $2\sqrt{st}$ D $\dfrac{4st}{s + t}$

E   more information needed

Senior Challenge 2001

1. A candle will burn for 100 hours. If I light it at midday on Sunday, on which day will it burn out?

    A Tuesday   B Wednesday   C Thursday   D Friday   E Saturday

2. Exactly one of the following numbers is divisible by 11. Which is it?

    A $10^7 - 11$ B $10^7 - 1$ C 10^7 D $10^7 + 1$ E $10^7 + 11$

3. The diagram shows a regular hexagon divided up into six equilateral triangles. How many quadrilaterals are there in the diagram?

    A 6   B 8   C 10   D 12   E 14

4. In the Hackey Hockey league, a team scores 5 points for a win, 2 for a draw and 0 if it loses. The Hickey Hockey Club has played 20 games in this league and has scored 21 points. What is the smallest possible number of games it could have lost?

    A 11   B 12   C 13   D 14   E 15

5. Goldbach's conjecture, which has not been proved, states that every even number greater than two is the sum of two primes. However, the same is not true for every odd number. Which of the following odd numbers is *not* the sum of two primes?

    A 13   B 33   C 43   D 53   E 73

6. The mean of seven consecutive odd numbers is 21. What is the sum of the first, third, fifth and seventh of these numbers?

    A 16   B 21   C 84   D 147   E more information needed

7. A gardener has a field in the shape of an isosceles triangle. He decided to plant it with rose bushes with the aid of his apprentice. He planted the first row with 101 bushes along the base, then his apprentice planted the next row with 100 bushes. They continued in this way, planting alternate rows, until the whole field was planted. The gardener planted the last row, which contained 1 bush.

    How many more bushes did the gardener plant than the apprentice?

    A 100   B 101   C 49   D 50   E 51

8. *ABCDEF* is a regular hexagon of area 60. What is the area of the kite-shaped figure *ABCE*?

    A $20\sqrt{3}$ B 40   C 49   D 50   E 51

9. Which of the following numbers n gives a counter-example for the statement: 'If n is a prime number then $n^2 + 2$ is also a prime number'?

    A 3   B 5   C 6   D 9   E none of them

10. The digits 1 to 8 are to be inserted in the grid on the right so that any two digits which are adjacent to each other in the sequence 1 to 8 are not adjacent to each other in the grid horizontally, vertically or diagonally. Which one of the following digits could be placed in the box labelled **X**?

A 4   B 5   C 6   D 7   E 8

11. Given that $x = \frac{1}{y}$, where x and y are unequal and non-zero, which of the following is always equal to $\left(x + \frac{1}{x}\right)\left(y - \frac{1}{y}\right)$?

A $y^2 - x^2$ B $x^2 - y^2$ C $2y$ D $2x$ E 0

12. The diagram shows a 2×2 square and a 3×1 rectangle. One vertex of the square lies on a side of the rectangle. The sides of the rectangle are parallel to the diagonals of the square. What is the area of the shaded triangle?

A $\frac{1}{2}$ B 1 C $\frac{3}{2}$ D 2 E $\frac{5}{2}$

13. Rosie the road-runner recently ran in two road races. The second race was 20% further in distance than the first race and Rosie's average speed was 20% slower in the second race. By what percentage was her time for the second race greater than that for the first?

A $33\frac{1}{3}\%$ B 40%   C 44%   D 50%   E $66\frac{2}{3}\%$

14. The diagram shows a square and two equilateral triangles. All the sides have length 1. What is the length of XY?

A $\sqrt{3}-1$ B $\frac{2}{3}$ C $\frac{3}{4}$ D $\frac{\sqrt{3}}{2}$ E $\frac{2+\sqrt{3}}{4}$

15. Sam correctly calculates the value of $5^8 \times 8^5$. How many digits does her answer contain?

A 11   B 12   C 13   D 14   E 15

16. A traffic cone is painted with red (R) and white (W) bands of paint as shown. The sloping heights of the bands are in the ratio $1 : 3 : 2$. What is the ratio of the area painted white to the area painted red?

A 5:9   B 5:7   C 1:1   D 7:5   E 9:5

17. Last year, a newspaper reported the results of a survey: 'Children in the U.K. get £3.10 pocket money a week on average. Scottish parents are the most generous, giving £5.35 a week.' Assuming that Scottish children made up 10% of the survey, what was the average pocket money per week in the rest of the U.K.?

A £0.85   B £1.85   C £2.85   D £3.85   E £4.85

18. Which of the curves or lines given by the following equations comes closest to the origin?

A $y = x - 4$ B $x^2 + y^2 = 4$ C $y = \frac{4}{x}$ D $y = x^2 + 4$ E $y = x^4 - 4$

19. Note that $2001 = 3 \times 23 \times 29$. What is the number of the next year which can be written as the product of three distinct primes?

   A   2002   B   2004   C   2006   D   2007   E   none of these

20. In the diagram, AB, CB and XY are tangents to the circle with centre O and $\angle ABC = 48°$.
   What is the size of $\angle XOY$?

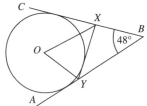

   A   42°   B   69°   C   66°   D   48°   E   84°

21. A postman's sack contains five letters, one each for the five houses in Cayley Close. Mischievously, he posts one letter through each door without looking to see if it is the correct address. In how many different ways could he do this so that exactly two of the five houses receive the correct letters?

   A   5   B   10   C   20   D   30   E   60

22. For how many values of n are both n and $4^{\left(\frac{n-1}{n+1}\right)}$ integers?

   A   1   B   2   C   3   D   4   E   5

23. An equilateral triangle is inscribed in a circle, as shown. Another equilateral triangle is drawn in one of the segments so that the final diagram has a line of symmetry.
   What is the ratio of the length of the side of the bigger triangle to the length of the side of the smaller triangle?

   A $(\sqrt{5}+1):1$ B $(2\sqrt{5}+1):1$ C $(\sqrt{3}+\sqrt{5}):1$ D $2\sqrt{5}:1$ E $3:1$

24. The Queen of Hearts had some tarts, but they were eaten. Precisely one of the following statements about the tarts and the Knaves of Clubs, Diamonds and Spades is true. Which one?
   A   None of the three Knaves ate any tarts.
   B   The Knave of Clubs ate some tarts.
   C   Only one of the three Knaves ate any tarts.
   D   At least one of the Knave of Diamonds and the Knave of Spades ate no tarts.
   E   More than one of the three Knaves ate some tarts.

25. The black triangle is drawn, and a square is drawn on each of its edges. The three shaded triangles are then formed by drawing three lines which join vertices of the squares and a square is now drawn on each of these three lines. The total area of the original three squares is A_1, and the total area of the three new squares is A_2. Given that $A_2 = kA_1$ then

   A $k = 1$ B $k = \frac{3}{2}$ C $k = 2$ D $k = 3$ E   more information needed

Senior Challenge 2002

1. How many squares of area 1 cm² have a total perimeter length which is equal to the perimeter of a single square of area 4 cm² ?

   A 2   B 4   C 8   D 16   E 32

2. Which of the following networks is not traversable? (A traversable network is one which can be drawn without taking the pen off the paper and without going over any line more than once.)

   A   B   C   D   E

3. Peri the winkle starts at the point (1, 1). Each day Peri crawls from point (x, y) to point $(y, x + y)$, so that at the end of the first day Peri has reached (1, 2).
   Where is Peri at the end of the sixth day?

   A (6, 7)   B (6, 12)   C (13, 21)   D (21, 34)   E (144, 233)

4. What is the remainder when 123456789 × 987654321 is divided by 6 ?

   A 1   B 2   C 3   D 4   E 5

5. The value of the product $wxyz$ is 2002 and w, x, y and z are prime numbers. What is the value of $w^2 + x^2 + y^2 + z^2$?

   A 66   B 203   C 260   D 285   E 343

6. In the village of Much-Pedling-in-the-Marsh, one third of the children can swim, two thirds can ride a bicycle and one seventh can both swim and ride a bicycle (though not necessarily at the same time). Given that there are fewer than 40 children in Much-Pedling-in-the-Marsh, how many of them can neither swim nor ride a bicycle?

   A 1   B 2   C 3   D 4   E 5

7. This crossnumber must be completed so that there is a different non-zero digit in each square. Which digit goes in the square marked **X** ?

1.	2.
3.	X

   Clues

   Across
   1. Cube
   3. Sum of two squares

   Down
   1. Square
   2. Prime

   A 1   B 3   C 5   D 7   E 9

8. A furlong is 220 yards long and a yard is 36 inches. A chain is 44 cubits long and a cubit is 54 barleycorns. There are 10 chains in a furlong. How many barleycorns are there in one inch?

   A 6   B 5   C 4   D 3   E 2

9. When forest trees are planted 1 metre apart in a particular repeating pattern, covering a large area of ground, the density of trees is about 10 000 per hectare.
   If, instead, the trees were planted 2 metres apart in the same pattern, approximately how many trees per hectare would there be?

   A 2 500   B 5 000   C 10 000   D 20 000   E 40 000

10. The diagram shows a triangular piece of paper that has been folded once to produce a shape with the outline of a pentagon.

   If a *rectangular* piece of paper is folded once, what is the smallest value of n (greater than 4) for which it is not possible to create an n-sided polygon in the same way?

   A 6   B 7   C 8   D 9   E 10

11. The diagram shows two concentric circles of radii r and $2r$ respectively. What is the ratio of the total shaded area to the total unshaded area?

   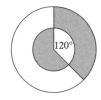

   A 5:7   B 7:5   C 1:1   D 2:3   E 3:2

12. At Ulan Bator market yesterday, you could buy a white elephant or 99 wild geese for the same number of Tugriks (the Mongolian currency). Today, the price of a white elephant has fallen by 10% and the price of a wild goose has risen by 10%. How many wild geese are now worth the same as one white elephant?

   A 81   B 90   C 98.01   D 99   E 121

13. The cards in a set of 36 are numbered 1 to 36. The cards are shuffled and four cards are dealt. What are the chances of them being dealt in descending order?

   A 1 in 2   B 1 in 8   C 1 in 16   D 1 in 24   E 1 in 36

14. A circular disc of diameter d rolls without slipping around the inside of a ring of internal diameter $3d$, as shown in the diagram. By the time that the centre of the inner disc returns to its original position for the first time, how many times will the inner disc have turned about its centre?

   A 1   B π C 3   D 2π E 2

15. For how many integer values of n does the equation $x^2 + nx - 16 = 0$ have integer solutions?

   A 2   B 3   C 4   D 5   E 6

16. Three circles touch, as shown in the diagram. The two larger circles both have radius 1 and the smaller circle has radius $\sqrt{2} - 1$. What is the perimeter of the shaded region?

   A $\frac{\pi}{4}(\sqrt{2} - 1)$ B $\frac{\pi}{2}(\sqrt{2} - 1)$ C $\frac{\pi}{2}$ D $\frac{\pi}{4}(\sqrt{2} + 1)$ E $\frac{\pi}{\sqrt{2}}$

17. I have a ten volume collection of mathematical puzzles. Each volume contains the same number of puzzles and the puzzles are numbered consecutively throughout (so, for example, the number of the first puzzle in volume 2 is one more than that of the last puzzle in volume 1). Whilst browsing one night, I was particularly intrigued by puzzle number 351 in volume 5 and puzzle number 689 in volume 8. How many puzzles are there in each volume?

   A 70   B 71   C 85   D 87   E more information needed

18. When $n = 81$, what is the value of $\dfrac{n^{20}}{3^n}$?

    A less than $\frac{1}{100}$ B $\frac{1}{3}$ C 1   D 3   E more than 100

19. A sculpture consists of a row of 2 metre rods each placed with one end resting on horizontal ground and the other end resting against a vertical wall. The diagram shows how the rods BT, CU, DV, ... look from above. The bases of the rods B, C, D, ... lie on a straight line on the ground at 45° to the wall. The top ends of the rods T, U, V... lie on part of a curve on the wall. What curve is it?

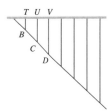

    A a straight line   B a parabola   C a circle   D a sine curve   E a quartic curve

20. Which of the following could be the graph of $y = \sin(x^2)$?

21. In the figure, PQ and RS are tangents to the circle. Given that $a = 20$, $b = 30$ and $c = 40$, what is the value of x ?

    A 20   B 25   C 30
    D 35   E 40

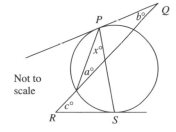

    Not to scale

22. Given that $y = \dfrac{x}{x + \dfrac{x}{x + y}}$, for which of the following values of x is y not a real number?

    A −6   B −3   C 1   D 3   E 6

23. A square $XABD$ of side length 1 is drawn inside a circle with diameter XY of length 2. The point A lies on the circumference of the circle. Another square $YCBE$ is drawn. What is the ratio of the area of square $XABD$ to the area of square $YCBE$?

    A 1 : 2   B 1 : 3   C 1 : $\sqrt{2}(2 - \sqrt{3})$ D 1 : $(\sqrt{2} - 1)$ E 1 : $(2 - \sqrt{3})$

24. A function f has the property that $f(n + 3) = \dfrac{f(n) - 1}{f(n) + 1}$ for all positive integers n.

    Given that $f(2002)$ is non-zero, what is the value of $f(2002) \times f(2008)$?

    A 1   B −1   C 2   D −2   E more information needed

25. Let N be a positive integer less than 10^{2002}. When the digit 1 is placed after the last digit of N, the number formed is three times the number formed when the digit 1 is placed in front of the first digit of N. How many different values of N are there?

    A 1   B 42   C 333   D 667   E 2002

Senior Challenge 2003

1. If you kept counting back eleven years at a time from 2003, at which of the following years would you arrive?

   A 1505   B 1605   C 1705   D 1805   E 1905

2. Triangle PQU has a right angle at U. The points R, S and T divide the side QU into quarters. Which of the following statements about the areas of the triangles PQR, PRS, PST, PTU is true?

   A All have the same area   B $\triangle PQR$ is biggest   C $\triangle PRS$ is biggest

   D $\triangle PST$ is biggest   E $\triangle PTU$ is biggest

3. If $a \oplus b = \sqrt{ab} + 4$, then what is the value of $(2 \oplus 6) \oplus 8$?

   A 6   B 8   C 10   D 12   E 18

4. Susan is taller than Sophie, but shorter than Sandra. Stephanie is taller than Sarah, but shorter than Susan. Who is the tallest of these five girls?

   A Susan   B Sophie   C Sandra   D Stephanie   E Sarah

5. One of the oldest sporting events in the world is the Kiplingcotes Derby, a horse race which has been held in the East Yorkshire Wolds almost every year since 1519. Each rider pays a fee of £4.25 to enter the race. The first prize in the race is the sum of £50, but the second prize is the total of the entry fees minus an administration cost of 25p per rider. In 2000, 18 riders competed in the Kiplingcotes Derby. How much greater than the first prize was the second prize?

   A £22   B £26.50   C £46   D £72   E £76.50

6. The engineering company, Sparks and Tensor, has a complicated system of conveyor belts in its factory. Components must travel along these belts in the directions shown by the arrows.

   How many different routes are there from A to F along the conveyor belts?

   A 4   B 5   C 6   D 7   E 8

7. Climbers use ropes of different diameters. A 50m rope which is 9mm in diameter weighs about 2.7kg. Roughly what would a 50m rope of the same material, but of diameter 11mm, weigh?

   A 2.7kg   B 3.3kg   C 4kg   D 4.9kg   E 6kg

8. The difference between two numbers is one quarter of their sum. What is the ratio of the smaller number to the larger number?

   A $3:8$ B $1:2$ C $5:7$ D $1:4$ E $3:5$

9. Mary received a 10% pay rise, and Margaret received a 5% pay rise. This gave them both salaries of £23 100 per year. How much more, per year, did Margaret earn than Mary before they received these pay rises?

   A £1155   B £1000   C £850   D £760   E £550

10. On 2 July 2002, Steve Fossett completed the first solo balloon circumnavigation of the world after $13\frac{1}{2}$ days. Assuming the balloon travelled along a circle of diameter 12 750 km, roughly what was the average speed of the balloon in km/h?

A 12 B 40 C 75 D 120 E 300

11. In a fit of madness, the bee Zerk left the hive and flew 1m due North, then 1m due East, then 1m vertically up. She then made a beeline for the hive, flying directly home in a straight line.

How far, in m, did she fly altogether?

A 4 B $3 + \sqrt{2}$ C $3 + \sqrt{3}$ D $5\frac{1}{4}$ E 6

12. From the information given in the diagram shown alongside, what is the value of $a + b$?

A 3 B 4 C 5 D 6 E 7

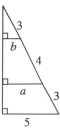

13. Which of the following is divisible by 3 for every whole number x?

A $x^3 - x$ B $x^3 - 1$ C x^3 D $x^3 + 1$ E $x^3 + x$

14. Which of the following straight lines should be omitted to leave four lines which determine a square?

A $y + x = 3$ B $y = x - 1$ C $y + x = 1$ D $y = x + 1$ E $y + x = 2$

15. The number of this year, 2003, is prime. How many square numbers are factors of 2003^{2003}?

A 0 B 1 C 44 D 1002 E 2003

16. Five peaches, three oranges and two melons cost £3.18. Four peaches, eight oranges and three melons cost £4.49. How much more expensive is a peach than an orange?

A 8p B 7p C 6p D 5p E more information needed

17. In the diagram alongside, square $ABCD$ has side 4cm, and square $AEFG$ has side 2cm.

What, in cm, is the length of CE?

A 4 B $4 + \sqrt{2}$ C 6 D 7 E $4 + 2\sqrt{2}$

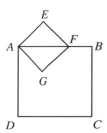

18. What is the value of $2^{2003} - 2^{2002} - 2^{2001} - 2^{2000}$?

A -2^{2002} B 0 C 2^{-4000} D 64 E 2^{2000}

19. The straight line shows the graph of $\frac{1}{y}$ plotted against $\sqrt{x}$. Which of the following could be a possibility for the equation linking y and x?

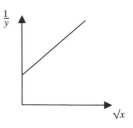

A $y^2 = \dfrac{1}{x - 1}$ B $y^2 = \dfrac{1}{x^2 + 1}$ C $y^2 = x - 1$

D $y^2 = \dfrac{1}{x - 2\sqrt{x} + 1}$ E $y^2 = \dfrac{1}{x + 2\sqrt{x} + 1}$

20. All six vertices of hexagon $UVWXYZ$ lie on the circumference of a circle; $\angle ZUV = 88°$ and $\angle XYZ = 158°$. What is the size of $\angle VWX$?

A $92°$ B $114°$ C $120°$ D $132°$ E it is impossible to determine

21. The outer equilateral triangle has area 1. The points A, B, C are a quarter of the way along the sides as shown. What is the area of the equilateral triangle ABC?

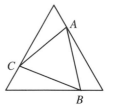

A $\dfrac{3}{8}$ B $\dfrac{7}{16}$ C $\dfrac{1}{2}$ D $\dfrac{9}{16}$ E $\dfrac{5}{8}$

22. Given an unlimited supply of 50p, £1 and £2 coins, in how many different ways is it possible to make a sum of £100?

A 1326   B 2500   C 2601   D 5050   E 10 000

23. The cube, $XYZTABCD$, is cut into four pieces by cutting along two planes, $BCTX$ and $BDTY$. What fraction of the volume of the cube is occupied by the piece containing corner A?

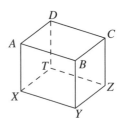

A $\dfrac{3}{8}$ B $\dfrac{1}{3}$ C $\dfrac{3}{10}$ D $\dfrac{5}{18}$ E $\dfrac{1}{4}$

24. AOB is an isosceles right-angled triangle drawn in a quadrant of a circle of radius 1 unit. The largest possible circle is drawn in the minor segment cut off by the line AB. This circle has radius r. The radius of the inscribed circle of the triangle AOB is R. What is the value of $\frac{R}{r}$?

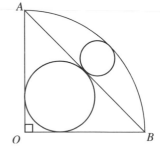

A 2   B $2\sqrt{2} - 1$ C $\sqrt{2} + 1$

D $\dfrac{9}{5}$ E $\sqrt{3}$

25. How many pairs of positive integers (x, y) are solutions of the equation $\dfrac{1}{x} + \dfrac{2}{y} = \dfrac{3}{19}$?

A 0   B 1   C 2   D 3   E more than 3

Senior Challenge 2004

1. Three different positive integers add up to 12. How large could the largest of the three numbers be?

    A 6   B 7   C 8   D 9   E 10

2. A dictionary defines one billion to be either one million million or one thousand million. What is the difference between these two numbers?

    A 1000   B 1 000 000   C 999 000

    D 999 000 000   E 999 000 000 000

3. Milly and Molly are each given a 100g ice-lolly. They start eating their lollies at the same time, but Milly eats hers twice as fast as Molly. When Molly has three times as much of her lolly left as has Milly, what fraction of her lolly has Milly eaten?

    A $\frac{1}{2}$ B $\frac{2}{3}$ C $\frac{3}{4}$ D $\frac{4}{5}$ E $\frac{5}{6}$

4. A pieman sells pies at 4p for 5, or 1p each. If Simon simply buys 2004 pies, what is the least amount he could pay?

    A £4.04   B £8.04   C £12.04   D £16.04   E £20.04

5. The first two scales shown are perfectly balanced. How many squares will be needed on the right of the third scales so that the scales balance?

    A 12   B 10   C 9   D 8   E 7

6. Pat's age is a prime number. Ten years ago, as a teenager, Pat's age was also a prime number. How old is Pat?

    A 17   B 23   C 27   D 29   E more information needed

7. A ball is dropped out of a classroom window onto the playground 29 feet 3 inches below. Every time the ball hits the ground it bounces to two thirds of its previous height. What is the greatest height to which it rises following the third bounce?

    A 1 foot 1 inch   B 3 feet 3 inches   C 8 feet 8 inches

                D   13 feet   E   13 feet 5 inches

8. The diagram shows three right-angled triangles. What is the value of x?

    A 14   B $10\sqrt{2}$ C 15

    D $12\sqrt{2}$ E $10\sqrt{3}$

9. How many numbers from 12 to 12345 inclusive have digits which are consecutive and in increasing order, reading from left to right?

    A 10   B 13   C 18   D 22   E 25

10. The diagram shows seven circles of equal radius which fit snugly in the larger circle. What is the ratio of the unshaded area to the shaded area?

A 7:1   B 7:2   C 2√3:1 D   9:2   E 1:1

11. Sam can mow a lawn in 3 hours. Mel takes 4 hours to mow the same lawn, and Chris takes 6 hours to do the same. If they work with a lawn mower each, and do not get in the way of each other, how long would they take to mow the lawn together?

A 1 hour 20 minutes   B 1 hour 30 minutes C   3 hours

D   4 hours 20 minutes   E 13 hours

12. One face of a solid polyhedron is a regular hexagon. What is the smallest possible number of edges the polyhedron could have?

A 7   B 9   C 12   D 15   E 18

13. The value of $1^{2004} + 3^{2004} + 5^{2004} + 7^{2004} + 9^{2004}$ is calculated using a powerful computer. What is the units digit of the correct answer?

A 9   B 7   C 5   D 3   E 1

14. L, M and N are midpoints of the sides of a skeleton cube, as shown. What is the value of angle LMN?

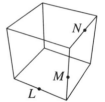

A 90°   B 105°   C 120° D   135° E 150°

15. The trunk of a monkey-puzzle tree has diameter 40 cm. As a protection from fire, the trunk of the tree has a bark which makes up 19% of its volume. On average, roughly how thick is the bark of the trunk?

A 0.4 cm   B 1.2 cm   C 2 cm   D 2.8 cm   E 4 cm

16. In triangle PQR, angle $P = 90°$, $PR = 15$ cm and $QR = 17$ cm. Circular arcs are drawn with centres at P, Q and R, and each arc touches the other two arcs.

What is the radius of the arc with centre R?

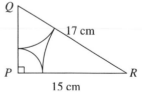

A 10 cm   B 10.5 cm   C 11 cm

D   11.5 cm   E   12 cm

17. The graph of $y = |f(x)|$ is shown. Given that the graph of $y = f(x)$ is a continuous curve, how many different possibilities are there for the graph of $y = f(x)$?

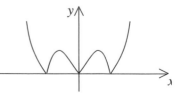

A 16   B 12   C 8

D 4   E 2

18. In the diagram, the line PQ is a tangent at N to the circle through points L, M and N. The lengths LM and LN are equal. The line LM produced meets the tangent PQ at the point R.

    If $\angle PNL = \theta°$, what is the value, in degrees, of $\angle LRP$?

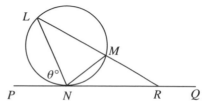

     A $3\theta - 180$ B $180 - 2\theta$ C $180 - \theta$ D $90 - \tfrac{1}{2}\theta$ E θ

19. The letters S, M and C represent whole numbers. If $S \times M \times C = 240$, $S \times C + M = 46$ and $S + M \times C = 64$, what is the value of $S + M + C$?

     A   19   B   20   C   21   D   24   E   36

20. Which is the lowest positive integer by which 396 must be multiplied to make a perfect cube?

     A   11   B   66   C   99   D   121   E   726

21. Triangle PQR has a right angle at Q and $PQ = QR$. The line through Q which divides the angle PQR in the ratio 1:2 meets PR at S. What is the ratio $RS:SP$?

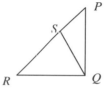

     A $\sqrt{2}:1$ B $\sqrt{3}:1$ C $2:1$

           D $\sqrt{5}:1$ E $3:1$

22. In the trapezium shown (not to scale), XY is parallel to two sides and passes through the point of intersection of the diagonals. What is the length XY?

     A   8 cm   B   9 cm   C   10 cm   D   11 cm   E   12 cm

23. The number N is exactly divisible by 7. It has 4008 digits. Reading from left to right, the first 2003 digits are all 2s, the next digit is n and the last 2004 digits are all 8s. What is the value of n?

     A   4   B   5   C   0 or 3   D   2 or 9   E   1 or 8

24. The diagram (not to scale) shows two circles of radius 105 which are tangent to each other and to a circle of radius 14. What is the radius of the largest circle which can be placed in the shaded region?

     A   2   B   3   C   4

           D   5   E   6

25. Positive integers x and y satisfy the equation: $\sqrt{x + \tfrac{1}{2}\sqrt{y}} - \sqrt{x - \tfrac{1}{2}\sqrt{y}} = 1$. Which of the following is a possible value of y?

     A   5   B   6   C   7   D   8   E   9

Senior Challenge 2005

1. What is the value of 2005 plus 2005 thousandths?

    A 2005.002005   B 2005.2005   C 2007.005   D 2025.05   E 2205.5

2. The number 2005 is the sum of a sequence of five consecutive positive integers. Which of the following numbers occurs in this sequence?

    A 395   B 400   C 405   D 410   E 415

3. What is the mean of the five numbers 1^5, 2^4, 3^3, 4^2 and 5^1 ?

    A 6.2   B 11.4   C 12.2   D 13   E 13.8

4. The diagram shows two squares, with sides of length 1 and 3, which have the same centre and corresponding sides parallel. What fraction of the larger square is shaded?

    A $\dfrac{4}{9}$ B $\dfrac{4}{11}$ C $\dfrac{2}{5}$ D $\dfrac{2}{7}$ E $\dfrac{6}{11}$

5. Last year Rachel took part in a swimathon. Every day for 9 weeks she swam the same number of lengths, either in a 25m indoor pool or a 20m outdoor pool. Later she discovered that she had swum the same total distance in each pool. On how many days did Rachel swim in the indoor pool?

    A 45   B 42   C 35   D 32   E 28

6. How many differently shaped triangles exist in which no two sides are the same length, each side is of integral unit length and the perimeter of the triangle is less than 13 units?

    A 2   B 3   C 4   D 5   E 6

7. Consider the arithmetic sequences 1998, 2005, 2012, … and 1996, 2005, 2014, …. Which is the next number after 2005 that appears in both sequences?

    A 2054   B 2059   C 2061   D 2063   E 2068

8. An examination paper is made by taking 5 large sheets of paper, folding the pile in half and stapling it. The pages are then numbered in order from 1 to 20. What is the sum of the three page numbers that are on the same sheet of paper as page number 5?

    A 13   B 21   C 33   D 37   E 41

9. What is the value of the expression: $(1 + \frac{1}{2})(1 + \frac{1}{3})(1 + \frac{1}{4})\ldots(1 + \frac{1}{2004})(1 + \frac{1}{2005})$?

    A 1001   B 1002   C 1003   D 1004   E 1005

10. Sam and Pat were counting their money. They discovered that if Sam gave Pat £5, then Pat would have 5 times as much as Sam, but if Pat gave Sam £5, then Sam would have 5 times as much as Pat. How much did they have altogether?

    A £10   B £15   C £20   D £25   E £30

11. A sculpture is made up of 12 wooden cylinders, each of height 2cm. They are glued together as shown. The diameter of the top cylinder is 2cm and each of the other cylinders has a diameter 2cm more than the one immediately above it. The exhibit stands with its base on a marble table. What, in cm², is the total surface area of the sculpture, excluding the base?

A 456π B 356π C 256π D 156π E 144π

12. The positive integer x is a multiple of 7, and $\sqrt{x}$ is between 15 and 16.   What is the number of possible values of x?

A 1   B 2   C 3   D 4   E 5

13. In the figure shown, what is the sum of the interior angles at A, B, C, D, E?

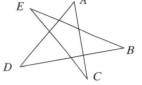

A 90°   B 135°   C 150° D   180°

  E more information required.

14. A square number is divided by 6. Which of the following could not be the remainder?

A 0   B 1   C 2   D 3   E 4

15. The four statements in the box on the right refer to a mother and her four daughters. One statement is true, three statements are false.

Who is the mother?

| Alice is the mother. |
| Carol and Ella are both daughters. |
| Beth is the mother. |
| One of Alice, Diane or Ella is the mother. |

A Alice   B Beth   C Carol   D Diane   E Ella

16. A hockey team consists of 1 goalkeeper, 4 defenders, 4 midfielders and 2 forwards. There are 4 substitutes: 1 goalkeeper, 1 defender, 1 midfielder and 1 forward. A substitute may only replace a player of the same category eg: midfielder for midfielder. Given that a maximum of 3 substitutes may be used and that there are still 11 players on the pitch at the end, how many different teams could finish the game?

A 110   B 118   C 121   D 125   E 132

17. Eight identical regular octagons are placed edge to edge in a ring in such a way that a symmetrical star shape is formed by the interior edges. If each octagon has sides of length 1, what is the area of the star?

A 5 + 10$\sqrt{2}$ B 8$\sqrt{2}$ C 9 + 4$\sqrt{2}$ D 16 − 4$\sqrt{2}$ E 8 + 4$\sqrt{2}$

18. A cube exactly fits inside a sphere and another sphere exactly fits inside this cube. What is the ratio of the volume of the smaller sphere to the volume of the larger sphere?

A 1 : 3$\sqrt{3}$ B 1 : 4   C 1 : 3   D 2 : 3   E 1 : 2

19. The graph of $y = |x|$ is shown alongside.
Which of the following could be a sketch of the graph of
$y = x|x|$?

A   B   C   D   E

20. It takes two weeks to clean the 3312 panes of glass in the 6000m² glass roof of the British
Museum, a task performed once every two years. Assuming that all the panes are
equilateral triangles of the same size, roughly how long is the side of each pane?

A   50 cm   B   1 m   C   2 m   D   3 m   E   4 m

21. What is the sum of the values of n for which both n and $\dfrac{n^2 - 9}{n - 1}$ are integers?

A   −8   B   −4   C   0   D   4   E   8

22. Given that $S = (x + 20) + (x + 21) + (x + 22) + \ldots + (x + 100)$, where x is a positive integer,
what is the smallest value of x such that S is a perfect square?

A   1   B   2   C   4   D   8   E   64

23. The diagram shows four touching circles, each of which also touches the
sides of an equilateral triangle with sides of length 3.
What is the area of the shaded region?

A $\dfrac{11\pi}{12}$ B π C $\dfrac{(4 + \sqrt{3})\pi}{6}$ D $\dfrac{(3 + \sqrt{3})\pi}{4}$ E $\dfrac{37\pi}{36}$

24. The factorial of n, written $n!$, is defined by $n! = 1 \times 2 \times 3 \times \ldots \times (n - 2) \times (n - 1) \times n$.
For how many positive integer values of k less than 50 is it impossible to find a value of n
such that $n!$ ends in exactly k zeros?

A   0   B   5   C   8   D   9   E   10

25. Which of the following is equal to $\dfrac{1}{\sqrt{2005 + \sqrt{2005^2 - 1}}}$?

A $\sqrt{1003} - \sqrt{1002}$ B $\sqrt{1005} - \sqrt{1004}$ C $\sqrt{1007} - \sqrt{1005}$
D $\sqrt{2005} - \sqrt{2003}$ E $\sqrt{2007} - \sqrt{2005}$

Section 2

Answers and solutions

JMC solutions 1997

1. **C** Since there are four lamp posts, there are three gaps so the distance is 3×25 m.

2. **B** Together, a postcard and a stamp cost 29p so the total is £2.90 leaving £7.10 change from £10.

3. **A** Since the shaded sections are equal and each is half the unshaded section.

4. **D** A good strategy is to look for the product of the biggest digits. D is the largest (with E second largest).

5. **E** Kylie has four front thumbs and two back thumbs, a total of six. So, between them, ten koala bears should have 60 thumbs.

6. **B** Because it is the one option which does not appear in the question.

7. **E** When a number is a multiple of 3, the sum of its digits is also a multiple of 3. In order, the digit sums are 3, 9, 18, 30 and 35.

8. **D** The smallest possible number is 2 and the biggest is 9. All the numbers from 2 to 9 can be obtained giving 8 possible totals.

9. **E** $1 - \dfrac{3}{4} = \dfrac{1}{4}$ and $\dfrac{1}{4}$ goes into 4, sixteen times.

10. **C** There are 31 days in July. 31×300 g $= 9300$ g $= 9.3$ kg.

11. **B** Two colours are not enough because at each corner three faces come together. A cube can be painted with three colours by using a different colour for each pair of opposite faces.

12. **E** The height of the second bounce must be 3 times the height of the rebound after it, i.e. 27 cm. Similarly for the first bounce, so the initial height was 3×27 cm.

13. **C** Since each row and each column contains one 1, one 2 and one 3 in some order none of 1, 2, 3 can appear more than once in any row or column. So the number which would go into a must be 3 and N must be 1 and so M is not 1. Also the number in b must be 2. Hence M cannot be 2 (or 1) so it is 3 and $M + N = 4$.

b		M
a	2	N
1		

14. **D** In order, the values of the fractions are: $\dfrac{3}{5}, \dfrac{6}{5}, \dfrac{3}{10}, \dfrac{5}{4}, \dfrac{7}{6}$. Three of these are bigger than 1. The biggest has value $1\frac{1}{4}$.

15. A Donna has used 4 red cubes so she has 8 left. So, if it can be done, these 8 must go on the bottom row. The other rows need 4, 5, 6, 7 which can be done with blue, yellow, blue, yellow in that order.

16. B When Humpty thought the watch read $|5{:}2|$ it actually read $|2{:}5|$. Later, when it seemed to show $|0{:}5|$ the correct time was $|5{:}0|$. So the time elapsed was 2 hours and 10 minutes.

17. B The angle alongside 113° is 67°. So $x = 37° + 67°$.

18. A The shaded region is a triangle with base 2 cm and height 3 cm so its area is $\frac{1}{2} \times 2 \times 3$ cm^2 = 3 cm^2.

19. C To get thirty-six pages, the newspaper must have nine sheets. Opening the paper at the middle would show pages 18 and 19. Working back through the sheets would give pages 16 and 21, 14 and 23, 12 and 25 and then 10 and 27. On the other side of this sheet are pages 9 and 28.

20. A The sum of all the digits must be divisible by 3 so the covered ones must total 1, 4, 7, 10, 13, 16, 19. But the number has to be divisible by 4 and by 5 so the final pair of digits must be 00, 20, 40, 60, 80. The only pair which total to provide a multiple of 3 is 40.

21. D If the hall were full, then the amount collected would be £600 plus £2 for every adult. Since $1320 = 600 + 2 \times 360$ that would be 360 adults and 240 children. To create spare seats, bring in one more adult and remove three children. This works because
$361 \times 3 + 237 \times 1 = 1083 + 237 = 1320$.

22. B From 2pm to 4pm the amount covered was $\frac{3}{4} - \frac{1}{3} = \frac{9}{12} - \frac{4}{12} = \frac{5}{12}$. So for $\frac{1}{12}$, the time taken was 120 minutes $\div 5 = 24$ minutes. So $\frac{1}{3} = \frac{4}{12}$ would take 96 minutes so they set out 1hr 36min before 2pm.

23. D Rate for Jim is $12\frac{1}{2}$ km per litre. For Kim, the rate is 12km per litre and for Lim it is 13km per litre. So Lim is most economical, then Jim and then Kim.

24. C First notice that no prime numbers can be used so we exclude 113. Similarly, since $115 = 5 \times 31$ it cannot have any link. Now $119 = 7 \times 17$ so, if it is to fit in it will be best and one end (with 112 alongside). A possible sequence is 119, 112, 118, 116, 114, 111, 117 so only 113 and 115 need to be left out.

25. E $PU = 58$ and $RU = 40$ so $PR = 18$. $QV = 68$ and $SV = 53$ so $QS = 15$. So since $PS = 23$, $PQ = 8$. $PU = 58$ and $RU = 40$ so $PR = 18$ and $QR = 10$. $PS = 23$ and $PR = 18$ give $RS = 5$. $QT = 30$ and $QS = 15$ so $ST = 15$. $PU = 58$ and $PT = 38$ so $TU = 20$. Finally, $SV = 53$ and $SU = 35$ so $UV = 18$. Since this completes the individual sections, all the grid can be completed.

JMC solutions 1998

*C D B D E * B D A C D * B E C E A * B A C A E * E B B D C*

1. **C** 2 400 040 002 = 2 400 040 000 + 2. Since 2 400 040 000 is divisible by 5 the remainder when 2 400 040 002 is divided by 5 must be 2.

2. **D** From 1911 to 1998 is 87 years. In 1911, the tree was 62 years old so, in 1998, the tree is 62 + 87 = 149 years old.

3. **B** 2 × 17 + 3 × 17 + 5 × 17 give 10 × 17 = 170.

4. **D** There were two full bottles and two empty bottles. The two half full and two half empty are the same bottles. The one third full and one third empty ones are different so the total number is 2 + 2 + 2 + 2 + 2 = 10.

5. **E** The train left at 17.46 so it arrived 43 minutes later at 18.29.

6. **B** All arrows point to *K* so *Ko* is the youngest. All arrows point away from *J* so *Jo* is the oldest. Finally *Uo* is older than *Mo* who is older than *Co*. Hence the order is *KCMUJ*.

7. **D** If a prize had been numbered from 4 to 10, it would be easier to see that 7 items would be given. In this case, the essential numbers are the last three digits, 384 to 500. The answer is 500 − 383 = 117 five pound notes.

8. **A** $1998 = 2 \times 999 = 2 \times 3^2 \times 111 = 2 \times 3^3 \times 37$. So the different prime factors are 2, 3 and 37 which total 42.

9. **C** $\triangle + \bullet = *$ and $\triangle + \triangle + \bullet = * + \square + \square$ so $\triangle + * = * + \square + \square$ which means $\triangle = \square + \square$.

10. **D** Replacing the digits as specified the calculations become
A' 75 − 64   B' 85 − 74   C' 95 − 84   D' 05 − 94   E' 15 − 04.

11. **B** Because it is the only one which is less than a half.

12. **E**

13. **C** $25 = 9 + 9 + 7 = 9 + 8 + 8$. So the only combinations of three digits which can total 25 are 7, 9, 9 and 8, 8, 9. From 7, 9, 9, we can get 799, 979, 997 and from 8, 8, 9 we can get 988, 898, 889.

14. **E** The perimeter of both shapes is 200cm so the square is 50 cm × 50 cm. The areas are 2500 cm^2 and 2400 cm^2 so the difference is 100 cm^2.

15. **A** The perimeter is 12 m or 1200 cm. The total length of the worms would be about 510 × 20 cm = 10200 cm. So the nearest estimate is $8\frac{1}{2}$ times round.

16. **B** Five pings and five pongs are worth the same as two pongs and eleven pings. So five pings and three pongs equal eleven pings and thus three pongs equal six pings so one pong is worth the same as two pings.

17. A The cross in the second column must go into *Y* as the lower three places are diagonally or horizontally covered by *X*. The only square in the third column not covered by either *X* or *Y* is *A*.

18. C Adding the angles gives $6x - 120 = 180$ so $x = 50$ and the angles are 60°, 60°, 60°.

19. A Doing some reshading we have. So the shaded section is $\dfrac{5\frac{1}{2}}{8} = \dfrac{11}{16}$.

20. E *B* could have 2 and 10 with *A* having 4 and 7; *C* having 5 and 8 and *D* having 6 and 9. Alternatively, *A* could have 2 and 9, with *B* having 4 and 8; *C* having 6 and 7 and *D* having 5 and 10.

21. E MATHS gives $10 + 1 + 16 + 15 = 42$.
EQUALS gives $2 + 13 + 5 + 1 + 9 + 15 = 45$.
ALGEBRA gives $1 + 9 + 5 + 2 + 2 + 14 + 1 = 34$.
PLUS gives $12 + 9 + 5 + 15 = 41$.
GEOMETRY gives $5 + 2 + 4 + 10 + 2 + 16 + 14 + 20 = \cancel{63}.\ 73$

22. B Points in each event are $5 + 3 + 2 + 1 = 11$. After 6 events, 66 points have been awarded. The highest possible score is $6 \times 8 = 48$ (and the lowest 12). Possible scores seem therefore to be 42 and 24. We ought to check that these are attainable. $4 \times (1 + 2) + (1 + 3) + (3 + 5) = 4 \times 3 + 4 + 8 = 24$ so it is a possible score. The difference is $42 - 24 = 18$.

23. B

| quadrilateral | pentagon | hexagon | heptagon | octagon |

24. D Taking five slices we can see

20   8   12   8   20   68 remain.

25. C It is only necessary to consider blocks of 12 coins.

Initially	20	20	20	20	20	20	20	20	20	20	20	20
First	20	10	20	10	20	10	20	10	20	10	20	10
Second	20	10	5	10	20	5	20	10	5	10	20	5
Final	20	10	5	2	20	5	20	2	5	10	20	2

The bottom row totals $4 \times 20 + 2 \times 10 + 3 \times 5 + 3 \times 2 = 121$.
Continuing the pattern for a total of 5 blocks gives a total £6.05.

JMC solutions 1999

1.   **C**   Thirty-four hundredths = 0.34.

2.   **C**   200ml is approximately one third of a pint or just under two thirds of the volume of a typical can of soft drink (330ml).

3.   **A**   The hour hand will be half way between the 'one' and the 'two' whilst the minute hand will still point to the 'six'.

4.   **C**   7000000 is exactly divisible by 7, so we need only to calculate the remainder when 10 is divided by 7.

5.   **A**   There must be seven 26p stamps to give a total ending in 2.
$7 \times 26p$ = £1.82 and therefore there is only one 20p stamp.

6.   **B** $19 + 99 + 19 \times 99 = 99 + 19 \times 1 + 19 \times 99 = 99 + 19 \times 100 = 99 + 1900$
or $19 + 99 + 19 \times 99 = 19 + 99 \times 1 + 99 \times 19 = 19 + 99 \times 20 = 19 + 1980$

7.   **D**   There are eight people, each of whom buys seven eggs each.

8.   **E**   Total debt = £55 × 55 = £3025. £50 × 50 + £5 × 5 = £2525. I have £500 too little.

9.   **C**   Only 21 of the 22 slices may be used and these will make seven 'double-decker' sandwiches. Each sandwich requires four sides of bread to be buttered.

10.   **A**   Laa-laa's luggage is 15kg overweight. The limit above which a charge is made is therefore 35kg. Po's luggage weighs less than this and therefore she will not be charged.

11.   **C** $2 + 3 + 5 + 7 + 11 + 13 + 17 + 19 + 23 = 100$.
(By coincidence, the number of prime numbers less than 100 is 25.)

12.   **E**   There are 3 routes from S to U and 2 from U to V. The number of different routes from S to V is therefore $3 \times 2 = 6$. Each of these may be followed by any one of three different routes from V to T, making a total of $6 \times 3 = 18$ routes in all.

13.   **D** $\angle PMR = 110°$ (adjacent angles on a straight line); $\angle PRM = 50°$ (angle sum of a triangle) $\angle PRS = 130°$ (adjacent angles on a straight line).
(A shorter method uses the exterior angle theorem: $\angle PRS = \angle MPR + \angle PMR$.)

14.   **D**   Let Ross drink x ml. Then Rachel drinks $\frac{3}{2}x$ ml. $\frac{3}{2}x + x = 750 \Rightarrow \frac{5}{2}x = 750 \Rightarrow x = 300$. Rachel, therefore, drinks 450ml.

15.   **C**   The distance the snail moves East = $2 - 4 + 6 - 8 + 10 = 6$.
The distance the snail moves North = $1 - 3 + 5 - 7 + 9 = 5$.

16.   **D** $-1 + 4 = 3$; $2 + 2 = 4$; $1 + 6 = 5$; $2 + 6 = 8$.

17. **E**   A test for divisibilty by 11 is to add alternate digits:

$$1 + 3 + * + 7 = 11 + *; \quad 2 + 4 + 6 + 8 = 20.$$

If the original number is a multiple of 11 then these two totals will be the same or will differ by a multiple of 11. In this case, $11 + * = 20 \Rightarrow * = 9$.

Or, you can solve it without knowing a rule as follows:–

$$1234*678 = 12340678 + 1000* = (11 \times 1121879 + 9) + 11 \times 90* + 10*$$

and hence is divisible by $11 \Leftrightarrow 10* + 9$ is divisible by 11. So $* = 9$.

18. **B** $6729 \times 2 = 13458$ and therefore $\dfrac{6729}{13458}$ is equal to one half and uses all the digits from 1 to 9 inclusive.

19. **E**   The required fold lines are shown (A folds to A').

20. **E**   With the front face as shown, the cubes A – D would appear as shown:

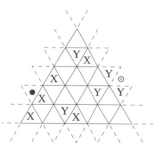

21. **D** $\frac{6}{7}$ of Granny's age is 84. Her age, therefore, is $84 \times \frac{7}{6} = 98$.

22. **D**   The hands are at right angles to each other twice in every hour except that the only time between 2.00 and 3.00 is just after 2.27 and the only time between 8.00 and 9.00 is just after 8.27.

23. **B**   In the diagram the triangles labelled X can be reached from • in one 'move'; those labelled Y are triangles which are one 'move' away from ⊙. This shows that it is not possible to go from • to ⊙ in one 'move', nor in two 'moves' since none of the triangles are labelled both X and Y. However, some of the triangles labelled Y may be reached from a triangle labelled X in one 'move' and therefore it is possible to complete the required task in three 'moves'.

24. **A**   Let the time which Boris takes to run up five steps be T. Therefore:

Boris takes $\frac{99}{5}T$ to run up the 99 steps;

Spike takes $\frac{78}{4}T$ to run up the $(99 - 21)$ steps;

Percival takes $\frac{61}{3}T$ to run up the $(99 - 38)$ steps.

$\frac{78}{4} < \frac{99}{5} < \frac{61}{3}$ and therefore the order is Spike, Boris, Percival.

25. **D**   The multiplication sum is 43×29.

There cannot be a carry from the units column into the tens column in the final addition and this tells us we have 860 on the fourth line. This must come from 43 multiplied by a number between 20 and 29 inclusive. The only single digit which multiplies 43 to give a three digit number with 8 as the middle digit (third row) is 9 and therefore we have

```
      4 3
  ×   2 9
    3 8 7
    8 6 0
  1 2 4 7
```

JMC solutions 2000

*E B B D A * D C C E B * D D B E A * D D C B E * A C A B E*

1.   E   Half of 999 = ½ (1000 −1) = 500 − ½ = 499½.

2.   B   2000 − 1642 = 358.

3.   B $x = 50 − 22$. This method uses the theorem:
An exterior angle of a triangle is equal to the sum of the two interior and opposite angles.

4.   D   The values are A 24   B 14   C 14   D 36   E 21.

5.   A   If UKMT is reflected in a horizontal mirror line directly below it then image A appears.

6.   D   A van load can take only two crates and hence twelve van loads will be required.

7.   C   12 hours and 15 minutes from 6:45 am will take the time to 7:00 pm and there will then be 29 minutes of the 12 hours and 44 minutes remaining.

8.   C   In C there is no connection between the pair of holes on the left of the card and the pair of holes on the right. There must, however, be such a connection for the display on the front of the card to be as shown.

9.   E   If three-quarters of the members are boys then one-quarter are girls and the number of boys is three times the number of girls.

10.   B   140 000 × 6 g = 840 000 g = 840 kg. *Almost one tonne!*

11.   D   The relevant years are 2, 11, 20, 101, 110, 200, 1001, 1010 and 1100.

12.   D   The total area of the four strips is 40 cm², but there are four squares, each of area 1 cm², where two strips overlap. Hence the area covered is (40 − 4) cm².

13.   B   The girls who travel by bus make up 12% (¼ of 48%) of the whole school and the corresponding figure for boys is 26% (½ of 52%). Hence 38% of the whole school travel by bus.

14.   E   In reverse, the stages which lead to 45 are: 45 ← 43 ← 34 ← 17.

15.   A   Let Dilly's age be x. Then Dally is $x + 7$. In four years time Dilly will be $x + 4$ and Dally will be $x + 11$. Therefore $x + 11 = 2(x + 4)$ and hence $x = 3$. Dilly is 3, Dally is 10 and the sum of their ages is 13.

16.   D   The number of words = 256 × 33 × 9 ≈ 250 × 300 = 75 000. The best estimate, therefore, is 76 000.

17.   D   If a number is divisible by 9, then the sum of its digits must also be a multiple of 9. The sum of the digits of $d6d41$ is $2d + 11$, which must be an odd number between 13 and 29 inclusive. The only odd multiple of 9 in this interval is 27.

18. C Let the distance between adjacent dots be one unit. Then a circle of radius $\sqrt{5}$ units whose centre is at the centre of the grid passes through eight dots, as shown.

19. B The difference between successive numbers in the list is $\frac{1}{3}\left(\frac{3}{4} - \frac{1}{2}\right) = \frac{1}{12}$. Therefore $y = \frac{3}{4} - \frac{1}{12} = \frac{2}{3}$.

20. E The total cost of four apples, four oranges and four bananas is £1.54 + £1.70 = £3.24. Hence the amount Mr. Bean would pay for one apple, one orange and one banana is £3.24 ÷ 4 = 81p.

21. A Each hour, Tock 's watch gains three minutes on Tick's watch. It will, therefore, take 20 hours before it is one hour ahead of it.

22. C Let the width and height of each block of wood be x and y respectively and the height of the table be h. Then: $h + x = y + 84$ and $h + y = x + 96$.

Add these two equations: $\qquad\qquad h + x + h + y = y + x + 84 + 96$

Subtracting $(x + y)$ from both sides: $\qquad\qquad 2h = 180$

$$\therefore \quad h = 90$$

23. A If 21 and 35 are factors of the number, then 3, 5 and 7 must all be included amongst its prime factors. This means that the required number must be a multiple of 105 and, as the complete list of factors of 105 is 1, 3, 5, 7, 15, 21, 35 and 105, the answer is 105.

(A number which is the product of three different prime numbers must have exactly eight factors. If p, q and r are all different prime numbers then the factors of pqr are 1, p, q, r, pq, pr, qr and pqr itself.)

24. B Exchanging the '2' and the '5', then the '2' and the '7' and, finally, the '2' and the '9' gives a display of 635792, which is a multiple of 4.

(A whole number is a multiple of 4 if, and only if, the number formed by its last two digits, in this case 92, is a multiple of 4. Can you prove this?)

25. E Comparing the leading diagonal and the second row:

$13 + c + e = 5 + c + 15$ and hence $e = 7$.

Comparing the top row and the third column:

$13 + a + b = b + 15 + e$ and hence $a = e + 2 = 9$.

Comparing the second row and the second column:

$a + c + d = 5 + c + 15$ and hence $d = 20 - a = 11$.

13	a	b
5	c	15
x	d	e

We now have:

13	9	b
5	c	15
x	11	7

Let the 'magic' total be T. Then: $T = 22 + b$

$T = 20 + c$

$T = 18 + x$

$T = b + c + x$.

Adding the first three of these equations:

$3T = 60 + b + c + x$

So: $3T = 60 + T$

Thus: $T = 30$.

Therefore

$x = 30 - 18 = 12$.

(Notice that the magic total, in this case 30, is three times the number in the middle of the magic square, in this case 10. Can you prove that this is always the case in a 3 × 3 magic square?)

So surely answer is x = 12

JMC solutions 2001

*E C A C C * D A E B A * E B D E C * B D B C D * E E B A D*

1.   **E**   The match lasted 95 minutes, i.e. 1 hour 35 minutes.

2.   **C**   There are 17 matches in the diagram. Three squares which meet only at corners will require 12 matches. Hence removing 5 matchsticks will achieve a suitable arrangement, such as that shown in the diagram.

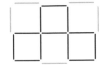

3.   **A**   It was 72 years from 1896 to 1968.

4.   **C**   50% of £60 = £30; 40% of £30 = £12.

5.   **C**   One eighteenth of 6 hours is one third of one hour, i.e. 20 minutes.

6.   **D**   As each offer of meat is worth the same amount, the most expensive individual item corresponds to the offer with the least number of items, i.e. a lamb cutlet.

7.   **A**   The diagram shows that the shape which the guinea-pig can reach is composed of a 10m × 20m rectangle and two semicircles of radius 10m whose centres are the ends of the bar.

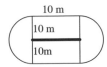

8.   **E**   The largest number is 0.9 and the smallest 0.17; their difference is 0.73.

9.   **B**   The star may be considered to be composed of four congruent right-angled triangles. The diagram shows that these may be arranged to fill one quarter of the large square completely.

10.   **A**   The number which will be reduced by the largest amount is that in which the digit 4 represents the greatest value. In the given numbers, the digit 4 represents 40000, 4, 400, 4000 and 40 respectively.

11.   **E**   In total, twelve goals were scored in the match. Therefore a winning margin of three goals is impossible since it would require one team to score an even number of goals and the other team an odd number. Results A to D could occur if the number of goals scored by Jokers and Jesters in the second half were, respectively, 3 and 4; 2 and 5; 1 and 6; 4 and 3.

12.   **B**   For each of the six colours, the leaflet may be folded in two different ways in which that particular colour is one of the two outside pages. This suggests that there are 12 different pairs of outside pages, but each possible pair has been counted twice in this calculation and hence there are six different pairs of outside pages.

13.   **D**   The octopus is able to open 8 jars per minute, so the number opened per hour is 60 × 8 = 480.

14.   **E**   Try it for yourself!

15.   **C**   The total number of toes per team is 5 × 12 = 60. There are 12 members in a team, so the mean number of toes per team member is $\dfrac{60}{12} = 5$.

16. B   If I pay the exact fare, the smallest number of coins I could use is 4 (2 × 20p and 2 × 2p). If I receive change, then it is not possible for only 2 coins to change hands since this would involve my giving the driver one coin (50p, £1 or £2) and receiving only one coin in change, but the necessary coin does not exist. However, if I give the driver a 50p coin and receive a 5p coin and a 1p coin in change, then only 3 coins change hands.

17. D   I can buy 18 (i.e. 6 × 3) lollipops for £1.80, leaving an additional 20p, with which I can buy one more lollipop.

18. B   Triangle PQR is equilateral; hence $\angle PRS = 60°$ and therefore $\angle XSQ = 40° + 60° = 100°$ (exterior angle of a triangle is equal to the sum of the two interior opposite angles). Hence, applying this result again, we deduce that $\angle SXT = (35 + 100)° = 135°$.

19. C $\dfrac{1}{12} + \dfrac{1}{24} = \dfrac{2+1}{24} = \dfrac{3}{24} = \dfrac{1}{8}$. Therefore $x = 8$.

20. D   The sum of the numbers from 1 to 9 inclusive is 45. As 1, 2 and 4 are each included in two of the lines, the sum of the individual totals of the four lines is $45 + 1 + 2 + 4 = 52$. Hence the total of the three numbers in each line is $52 ÷ 4 = 13$, so the * should be replaced by 8. One possible solution is shown on the right.

21. E   The values of 2^8 and 8^2 are 256 and 64 respectively and $256 ÷ 64 = 4$. Alternatively: $2^8 ÷ 8^2 = 2^8 ÷ (2^3)^2 = 2^8 ÷ 2^6 = 2^2 = 4$.

22. E   The length of the rectangle is to be increased by one third, whilst its height is to be decreased by one quarter. The cut in diagram E accomplishes this, as the diagram shows.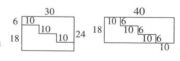

23. B   If Dilly brings two green gloves they will not necessarily be a matching pair since they could both be left-hand gloves or both be right-hand gloves and, similarly, two blue gloves could both be right-hand gloves. In the same way, three blue (or green) gloves could all be right-handed. However, if Dilly brings all four blue gloves then these will include a matching pair.

24. A   As the total number of squares in the two main diagonals is odd, the number of squares along each side of the pavement must also be odd. Let this number be n; there are n squares along each of the two main diagonals, but, as n is odd, one of these squares forms part of both diagonals and hence the total number of squares along the two main diagonals is $2n - 1$. Therefore $2n - 1 = 2001$ i.e. $n = 1001$.

Hence the required number of red tiles is $1001^2 - 2001 = 1\,000\,000$.

25. D   The combined grey and white areas form a square of side 11 and a square of side 7, a total area of 170. Similarly, the combined black and white areas form a square of side 9 and a square of side 5, a total area of 106. As the white area is included in both these totals, the difference between the totals will be the difference between the grey area and the black area. Hence the correct answer is $170 - 106 = 64$.

JMC solutions 2002

*A D C D A * A C E C E * E C A B D * C B D D B * A D C E B*

1. **A** $2000 \times 5 = 10\,000$ and $2 \times 5 = 10$ so $2002 \times 5 = 10\,000 + 10$.

2. **D** $3 + 6 \times 4 = 3 + 24 = 27 \neq 36$.

3. **C**   A is 12; B is 12; C is 15; D is 10 and E is 14.

4. **D**   As $\triangle ABC$ is equilateral $\angle BCA = 60°$. Since *JKLM* is a square, $\angle MJC = 90°$. So, since the angles of a triangle add up to 180°, $\angle JMC = 30°$.

5. **A**   Of the numbers 1, 2, 3, 4, 5, the only one which is a multiple of 5 is 5 itself.

6. **A**   The sum $= 5432100 + 1 + 2 + 3 + 4 + 5 = 5432115$.

7. **C**   The equal numbers cannot be 1 since $17 - 6 \times 1 = 11$, which is not a single digit number. Also they cannot be 3 or more as then the single digit would be negative. That leaves 2 which works since $17 - 6 \times 2 = 5$.

8. **E**   Each centre is 2.5 cm from the nearer end. So the distance between them is $(9 - 2 \times 2.5)$ cm.

9. **C**   The weight of the water poured out is $(21 - 12)$ kg. Thus the weight of the bucket is $(12 - 9)$ kg.

10. **E**   In our notation, the subtraction becomes $927 - 54$ which is 873. Su Erasmus would write this as 378.

11. **E**   The number of students in just the band is $60 - 12 = 48$. The number in just the orchestra is $20 - 12 = 8$. So the number in either band or orchestra (or both) is $(48 + 12 + 8)$.

12. **C**   Initially   1st move   2nd move   3rd move   4th move

So the area is that of a rectangle measuring 5m × 3m.

13. **A**   To be in this century, the number in the hundreds place must be zero so the same must be true for the number in the tens place. The last digit must equal the first. (The next palindromic year will be 2112.)

14. **B**   Inverting three glasses at a time means leaving one alone. In the sequence below, the first, the second, the third and then the fourth are left alone.

⊔⊓⊔⊓   ⊓⊓⊔⊔   ⊔⊔⊔⊓   ⊓⊓⊓⊓

So four moves will suffice.

One move is clearly not enough. Two moves either return to the start or leave 2 up and 2 down. Three moves leave 1 up or 3 up so the least number is 4 moves.

15. **D**   Since $\frac{3}{5} = 0.6 > 0.5$.

16. **C**   Initially   In mirror (when standing up)   After standing on her head!

FUN BEATRIX   ИUꟻ XIЯTAƎᗺ   ᗷE∀⊥IᴚX ꟻUИ

17. B   With no 5p coins, there could be 0, 1, 2, 3, 4 or 5 2p coins, i.e. 6 possible ways.
With one 5p coin, there could be 0, 1, 2 or 3 2p coins, i.e. 4 possible ways.
With two 5p coins, there can be no 2p coins, i.e. 1 possible way.

18. D

Unfold
about the
top edge

Now unfold
about the
right-hand edge

19. D

Number of sides	3	4	5	6	7	8	...
Number of diagonals	0	2	5	9	14	20	...

Or :– The number of corners to which a diagonal from a given corner can be drawn is $n - 3$. There are thus $n(n - 3)/2$ diagonals, the ½ because each diagonal has two ends. So $n(n - 3)/2 = 2n$. Cancelling one n from each side (since $n \neq 0$) we get $n - 3 = 4$ and so $n = 7$.

20. B   The sum of the length and breadth of the base is 8 cm and therefore we need to find two factors of 72 whose sum is 8 and whose product is also a factor of 72. We need consider only 1, 2, 3, 4 and 6 since these are the only factors of 72 less than 8. Of these, only 2 and 6 satisfy the above conditions. So the base of the cuboid is 2 cm × 6 cm and its height is 6 cm.

21. A   Since $\triangle ABC$ is isosceles, $\angle ABC = \angle BCA = y°$. As the exterior angle of a triangle is equal to the sum of the interior opposite angles, $x° = y° + z°$. Thus $z = x - y$.

22. D   Since when N is divided into 26, the remainder is 2, N is a factor of 24 but not of 26. The factors of 24 are 1, 2, 3, 4, 6, 8, 12, 24. Both 1 and 2 are factors of 26.
The sum of the other factors is $3 + 4 + 6 + 8 + 12 + 24 = 57$.

23. C   Since its circumference and each side of the triangle are both of length 1, the circle completes 1 revolution as it rolls along each of the three sides. In addition, at each vertex, the circle makes a one third turn and so, since there are three vertices, there are four revolutions in total.

24. E   Because AB ≠ DE, C ≠ 1. So C is 2 or more. Therefore A cannot be 3, 4 or 5 as D would be at least 6. So A = 1 or 2. If A = 2, then C is at least 3 and again D is at least 6. So A = 1.

$$\frac{\begin{array}{r} AB \\ \times\, C \end{array}}{DE}$$

Neither B nor C can be 5 as, if they were, E would have to be 0 or 5 but this also means that E is not 5. So D = 5. We can now see that, to get D = 5 we must have C = 4 and B × C must have two digits. So B = 3 and E = 2.

25. B

Questions answered	1	2	3	4	5	6	n
Time taken (seconds)	1	3	7	15	31	63	$2^n - 1$

One hour is 60 minutes which is 3600 seconds.
Since $2^{11} = 2048$, $2^{11} - 1 < 3600 < 2^{12} - 1$. So Gill answers the first 11 questions and obtains 55 marks.

JMC solutions 2003

*E D A B C * B C E B D * B A D C C * D E D D C * C E A B A*

1. **E** ½ of 199 = ½(200 − 1) = 100 − ½ = 99½.

2. **D** There are 100 teeth and 99 gaps so the length of the comb = 199mm = 19.9 cm.

3. **A** He will save 9 × 7 minutes.

4. **B** The task cannot be done by moving one plate, since removing any one plate from the formation of plates does not leave a formation which is part of the desired final formation. However, the 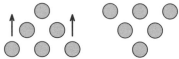 formation may be turned upside down, by moving two of the plates in the bottom row, as shown.

5. **C** The next time the six digits are all different, the meter will read 098671.

6. **B** Orange and yellow are B and D, though not necessarily in that order. Blue is E and, as orange is not next to blue, it cannot be D. So orange is B.

7. **C** Buying a bottle of juice, drinking the juice and returning the bottle involves a net cost of $1. Therefore, after doing this seven times, you will have $3 left i.e. just sufficient to buy an eighth bottle. After drinking the juice and returning this bottle, you will have $2 left, but this is not enough to buy a ninth bottle.

8. **E** When these numbers are divided by 9, the remainders are 5, 5, 5, 5 and 6 respectively.

   (*The digital root of a number is the sum of the digits of that number. If this is greater than 9, then the sum of its digits is found. If necessary, the procedure is repeated until a single digit is obtained. Sometimes called 'casting out nines', when a whole number is divided by 9, the remainder is the digital root of that number unless the digital root is 9, in which case the number is a multiple of 9 so the remainder is zero.*)

9. **B** The total age of the original four members is 4 × 19 = 76. When the fifth member joins, their total age is 76 + 24 = 100. So the mean age is now 100 ÷ 5 = 20.

10. **D** As 18 lies between 16 and 25, $\sqrt{18}$ lies between 4 and 5. Of the options available, only 4.2 is in this range. To confirm that 4.2 is correct (to one decimal place), we note that $4.15^2 = 17.2225$ and $4.25^2 = 18.0625$ so $\sqrt{18}$ lies between 4.15 and 4.25.

11. B   Let the cards intended for Carol, Holly and Ivy be C, H and I respectively. Nicolas can send Carol either H or I. In both cases, the recipients of the other two cards will then be determined as shown below.

Carol gets H, so Ivy gets C (as she cannot then get I) and Holly gets I.

or   Carol gets I , so Holly gets C (as she cannot then get H) and Ivy gets H.

12. A   Angles on a straight line add up to 180°. The base angles of the triangle are 67° and 71°. The angles of a triangle add to 180°. Therefore
$x = 180° - (67° + 71°) = 42°$.

13. D   As 2005 has units digit 5, 2005 is a multiple of 5. The sum of the digits of 2007 is 9, so 2007 is a multiple of 9; the sum of the digits of 2013 is 6, which means 2013 is a multiple of 3. This leaves 2009 and 2011. Now $2009 \div 7 = 287$ so four of the five options have been eliminated. To confirm that 2011 is prime, it is necessary to show that it is not a multiple of any prime less than $\sqrt{2011}$ and this is indeed the case.

14. C   As each number after the second is the sum of all the previous numbers in the sequence, each number after the third is double the previous number. So the first 10 terms of the sequence are 2, 3, 5, 10, 20, 40, 80, 160, 320, 640.

15. C   The information given suggests that each human swallows a spider while sleeping approximately once every nine years. Therefore the number of spiders consumed in this way in the UK in one year is approximately one ninth of 60 million, or approximately 7 million.

16. D   For C to give a units digit of 8 when multiplied by 7, its value must be 4. There is a carry of 2, so B must be 1 to give 9 in the tens column. There is no carry so 7 × 6 gives 2 in the hundreds column, i.e. E is 2, with a carry of 4. With this carry, A must be 5 to give 9 in the thousands column and there is a carry of 3 into the ten thousands column, so it is D that is 3.

17. E   The new rectangle will measure $(2a + 6)$ cm by 4 cm, so its area will be $(8a + 24)$ cm^2.

18. D   The single strip of paper forms a Möebius band which has only one surface, so all three 'UKMT's are written on the same side of the paper!

19. D   Let the number in the second cell be x. Then the sum of the numbers in the first and third cells is $2x$, so the number in the third cell is $2x - 8$. This means that $2x - 8$ is the mean of x and 20 so $x + 20 = 4x - 16$. Therefore $x = 12$. We can now deduce that the numbers are 8, 12, 16, 20 and 24.

(Note that the number in each cell is 4 more than that in the adjoining cell i.e. the numbers are in 'arithmetic progression'. One of the properties of such a sequence is that each term is the mean of the two terms on either side of it.)

20. C The grid may be considered to consist of four strips of wire of length a and five strips of length $\dfrac{3a}{4}$. So the total length required is $4a + 5 \times \dfrac{3a}{4} = \dfrac{31a}{4}$.

21. C From the starting square **S** the counter must first be moved to square A or square B. On the second move it must either go back to S, which is clearly not advisable, or to one of the squares C, D or E. Now to end at square T, the penultimate move must take the counter to either square X or square Y. As it is not possible to reach square X or Y in one move from any of squares C, D or E, the task must require at least five moves. One way of doing this is $S \rightarrow B \rightarrow E \rightarrow F \rightarrow X \rightarrow T$, although this is not the only possible five-move sequence.

22. E Consider what happens when both builders sell 60 bricks (60 is the LCM of 10 and 12). Bob will receive £36, while Geri will receive £35, so for every 60 bricks which each builder sells, Bob gains £1 more than Geri.

23. A As triangle ABC is isosceles, $\angle ABC = \angle ACB = w°$. Also, $\angle ABC = x°$ (vertically opposite angles) so $w = x$. Now triangle ACD is also isosceles, so $\angle DAC = \angle DCA = w° = x°$. We now see that the second statement is true as the three angles on the straight line at A have sizes $y°$, $x°$ and $z°$. In a triangle, an exterior angle is equal to the sum of the two interior opposite angles, so in triangle ABC: $\angle ABC + \angle ACB = z°$. Therefore $z = x + w = 2x$ (since $w = x$). Thus all three of the statements are true.

24. B The sum of three digits is at most 27, so the first digit of the house number is 4. Hence the second digit is less than 3. If this second digit were even, then the house number and the sum of its digits would have the same parity (i.e. both would be even or both would be odd), so their sum would be even. However, their sum is odd so the second digit is 1. Now if the last digit is d then $410 + d + (4 + 1 + d) = 429$, so $d = 7$ and the product of the digits is 28.

25. A The resulting shape will consist of six squares. Of these, two will have three 'cut' sides (sides which are formed by the cuts made along the edges of the cube and which as a result are not also sides of adjoining squares); two will have two 'cut' sides which are perpendicular to each other and two will have two 'cut' sides which are parallel to each other. Only shapes A and E satisfy these conditions. Furthermore, we note that the squares with three 'cut' sides both share a side with a square which has two 'cut' sides parallel to each other. Shape A satisfies this also, whereas shape E does not.

JMC solutions 2004

*B E A D C * E C E C B * D B A C D * C D B B A * E D E A D*

1. **B**   Of the letters in question, only S does not have at least one line of symmetry.

2. **E** $112 \div 7 = 16$. As none of the other options differs from 112 by a multiple of 7, 112 is the only one of these numbers which is exactly divisible by 7.

3. **A**   The required condition will next be met in 2014.

4. **D**   Every allowable route must pass through the centre point of the bow tie. There are two routes from P to the centre point, and for each of these there are two routes from the centre point to Q. So the total number of different routes $= 2 \times 2 = 4$.

5. **C**   Eighteen has 8 letters and 18 is not a multiple of 8. Of the other options, 6 is a multiple of 3, 12 is a multiple of 6, 70 is a multiple of 7 and 90 is a multiple of 6.

6. **E**   The differences between the given fractions and 1 are, respectively, $\frac{11}{23}, \frac{11}{34}, \frac{11}{45}, \frac{11}{56}$ and $\frac{11}{67}$. The smallest of these is $\frac{11}{67}$, so $\frac{56}{67}$ is nearest to 1.

7. **C**   There are 8 demisemiquavers in a crotchet and 4 crotchets in a semibreve, so there are 32 demisemiquavers in a semibreve.

8. **E**   The original pyramid had 8 edges. Cutting off the top corner adds 4 edges, whilst cutting off the other 4 corners adds 3 extra edges in each case. So the total number of edges is $8 + 4 + 4 \times 3 = 24$.

9. **C**   Pa Bean does not eat more than half the beans, so he eats at most 11 beans. Ma Bean eats the same number of beans as both children together, so she eats an even number of beans which is at least one quarter of the total number of beans eaten. Therefore she eats at least 6 beans. If she does eat 6 beans, then Pa Bean eats 11 beans, which is consistent with the information given. However, if Ma Bean eats 8 or more beans, then Pa Bean eats at most 7 beans and this is impossible as we are told that Pa Bean eats more beans than Ma Bean. So Pa Bean eats 11 beans.

10. **B**   The coins consisting of one of each type must add up to £1.25. The only way that this total may be made with coins of different denominations is by using a £1 coin, a 20p coin and a 5p coin.

11. **D**   The diagram shows the positions of the points after the rotations. Note that A_1, which is not marked, is the same point as A. Similarly, E_3, which is not marked, is the same point as E_2.

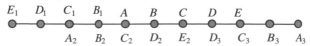

12. B   On Tuesday the White Rabbit will be 8 minutes late, on Wednesday 4 minutes late, on Thursday 2 minutes late and on Friday 1 minute late. So on the following Monday the White Rabbit will be 30 seconds late and on the day after that he will be 15 seconds late.

13. A   As $\angle QPR = 40°$, $\angle PQR + \angle PRQ = 180° - 40° = 140°$.
So $\angle SQR + \angle SRQ = 140° \div 2 = 70°$. Therefore $\angle QSR = 180° - 70° = 110°$.

14. C   The 8 individuals will each wrestle 6 others. This suggests that the number of bouts is $8 \times 6 = 48$. However, each bout has been counted twice in this calculation, so the number of bouts is $48 \div 2 = 24$.

15. D   After Thursday, two thirds of Granny's pension is left. So after she has spent one quarter of this amount on Friday, the fraction of the original amount which remains is three quarters of two thirds, i.e. one half.

16. C   The total angle turned through after each of the first 4 moves is $10°, 30°, 60°$ and $100°$. So the robot does not face due East at the end of a move in its first complete revolution. The total angle it has turned through after each of the next 5 moves is $150°, 210°, 280°, 360°$ and $450°$, so at the end of the 9th move the robot *does* face due East. As the robot moves 5m in each move, the distance it travels is 45m.

Note that this solution assumes that the robot is not starting the process close to the North Pole!

17. D   Statements such as those in this question may sometimes be shown to be false by considering the units digit of the expressions on each side. The units digit of $44^2 + 77^2$ is 5; the units digit of $55^2 + 66^2$ and hence also of $66^2 + 55^2$ is 1; the units digit of $88^2 + 33^2$ is 3 and that of $99^2 + 22^2$ is 5. So four of the statements are definitely false. It remains to check that $88^2 + 33^2 = 7744 + 1089 = 8833$.

18. B   Each of the 2004 squares, apart from those at the top and bottom of the shape, contributes 2 cm to the perimeter of the figure.
The other two squares contribute 3 cm each, so the perimeter is $(2002 \times 2 + 2 \times 3)\,\text{cm} = 4010\,\text{cm}$.

19. B   From the three equations we see that $(abc)^2 = 2 \times 24 \times 3 = 144$ and so, since abc is positive, $abc = 12$. Then the third equation tells us that $a = \frac{1}{2}$, the second that $b = 4$ and the first that $c = 6$. Therefore $a + b + c = 10\frac{1}{2}$.

20. A   As $PQRST$ is a regular pentagon, each of its internal angles is $108°$. The internal angles of the quadrilateral $PRST$ add up to $360°$ and so by symmetry $\angle PRS = \angle RPT = \frac{1}{2}(360° - 2 \times 108°) = 72°$. Each interior angle of a regular hexagon is $120°$, so $\angle PRU = 120°$.
Therefore $\angle SRU = \angle PRU - \angle PRS = 120° - 72° = 48°$.

21. E In total, the five pieces have four "holes" and six "tabs", so we can deduce that either B or E, both of which have two "tabs", will not be used.

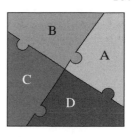

Shape A, therefore, is used and, after a clockwise rotation of 90°, will fit together with shape B. This suggests that it is shape E which is not used and shapes C and D will indeed complete the jigsaw after rotations of 90° and 180° anticlockwise respectively.

22. D In the four options other than D, the digits may be rearranged as follows:

A $21 \times 3 = 63$ B $18 \times 4 = 72$ C $38 \times 2 = 76$ E $29 \times 3 = 87$.

23. E Consider the thousands column. The letters represent different digits so, as S is 3, M is 2 and there is a carry of 1 from the hundreds column. Therefore A is 9, U is 0 and there is also a carry of 1 from the tens column. In the units column, $O + Y$ produces a units digit of 3, so $O + Y = 3$ or $O + Y = 13$. However, $O + Y = 3$ requires one of O, Y to equal zero (impossible as $U = 0$) or 2 (also impossible as $M = 2$). So $O + Y = 13$. We can also deduce that N is 8, since, in the tens column, $1 + 3 + N = 12$. The pairs of digits which produce a sum of 13 are 4 and 9, 5 and 8, 6 and 7. As A is 9 and N is 8, the only possible values for O and Y are 6 and 7. These are interchangeable, but in both cases $Y \times O = 42$.

24. A Let the length and breadth of each of the rectangles be a cm and b cm respectively. Then $2a = 3b$ and $a + b = 15$. So $2a + 2b = 30$. Therefore $3b + 2b = 30$, that is $b = 6$.

So the total area covered by the five rectangles is that of a rectangle measuring 18 cm by 15 cm, i.e. 270 cm^2.

25. D Let the first two terms of the sequence be a and b respectively. Then the next three terms are $a + b, a + 2b, 2a + 3b$. So $2a + 3b = 2004$. For a to be as large as possible, we need b to be as small as possible, consistent with their both being positive integers. If $b = 1$ then $2a = 2001$, but a is an integer, so $b \neq 1$.

However, if $b = 2$ then $2a = 1998$, so the maximum possible value of a is 999.

JMC solutions 2005

*C B C E B * D C A E D * A E A D A * D E A E B * D C B C B*

1.   C $1000 - 100 + 10 - 1 = (1000 - 100) + (10 - 1) = 900 + 9 = 909.$

2.   B   The original figure does not have a line of symmetry, so at least one match must be added. The figure shown, which is created by adding one extra match, does have a line of symmetry, so the smallest number of matches that need to be added is one.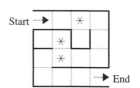

3.   C   As the number of days in a week is odd, Gollum will eat fish on alternate Mondays.

4.   E   Reflected in the mirror, the hands of the clock would have the same appearance at 1.30pm as they would normally have at 10.30pm.

5.   B   As the numbers are all positive, the largest number cannot be the difference between two of the others. Checking all the other options: $1 = 7 - 6$; $6 = 7 - 1$; $5 = 7 - 2$; $2 = 7 - 5$.

6.   D   The diagram shows the squares which Jonny's rat must visit more than once when it goes through the maze.

7.   C   Since one gram is the weight of half a million seeds, 1000 grams (i.e. one kilogram) is the weight of 500 million seeds.

8.   A   Let Reg have x grams of chocolate. Then the ratio of Peg's amount of chocolate to Meg's is $6x : 2x$, that is $3 : 1$.

9.   E   If the sheet of paper had been folded in half once then there would have been two holes in the unfolded sheet. Each additional fold doubles the eventual number of holes in the unfolded sheet so after four folds there will be sixteen holes.

10.   D   When Tilly woke on Thursday morning, she had learned fifteen new words, but had forgotten six of these, so she knew nine words. On Thursday, she learned five new words, so this was the first day on which she reached her target of fourteen words.

11. A The mode is the category which contains more than any of the others, so is represented by the largest sector in a pie chart.

12. E Remembering that, in the absence of brackets, multiplication is performed before addition, we see that $9 \times 6 + 73 = 54 + 73 = 127$, whereas $96 + 7 \times 3 = 96 + 21 = 117$. It is left as an exercise for the reader to check that the other four calculations are correct.

13. A As the squares are equal, the triangle in the figure is isosceles. So its angles are $70°$, $70°$ and $40°$. Hence $x = 360 - (40 + 90 + 90) = 140$.

14. D The fractions could be placed in order by writing them all with a common denominator of 630, or by writing them as decimal fractions. However, as they are all close in value to $\frac{1}{2}$, we may consider the value of each fraction minus $\frac{1}{2}$. These are, respectively, 0, $+\frac{1}{6}$, $+\frac{1}{10}$, $+\frac{1}{14}$ and $+\frac{1}{18}$. So, when they are placed in increasing order of size, the fractions are $\frac{1}{2}$, $\frac{5}{9}$, $\frac{4}{7}$, $\frac{3}{5}$ and $\frac{2}{3}$.

15. A The sum of the digits of each of the six numbers is 9. This means that they are all multiples of 9, so none of them is prime.

16. D $2005 \div 12 = 167$ remainder 1 so if 167 of the larger boxes are used, one bar will remain. If 166 of the larger boxes are used, 13 bars will remain and these cannot fill a whole number of smaller boxes. However, if 165 larger boxes are used, the 25 remaining bars will fill 5 smaller boxes. Using fewer than 165 larger boxes will increase the total number of boxes required since proportionately more of the smaller boxes would be needed, so the required number of boxes is $165 + 5$.

17. E There are two right-angled triangles which have their right angle at P: triangles UPQ and UPR. Similarly, there are two right-angled triangles in each case which have their right angle at R, S and U. There are three right-angled triangles which have their right angle at Q: triangles PQT, RQT and UQS. Similarly, there are three right-angled triangles which have their right angle at T, making 14 in all.

18. A The subtraction shows the number $10a + b$ subtracted from the number $10b + a$. Their difference is $9b - 9a$. So $9(b - a)$ has unit digit 6 and must therefore have value 36 since this is the only two-digit multiple of 9 which ends in 6. So c is 3. Note that the values of a and b are not unique. Provided that $b - a$ is 4, the difference of the two numbers will be 36, for example $51 - 15 = 36$; $62 - 26 = 36$; $73 - 37 = 36$ etc.

19. E Let the length and breadth of one of the original cards be l and b respectively. Then the lengths of the six sides of the 'L' shape (moving clockwise from the bottom left-hand corner) are l, b, $l - b$, $l - b$, b, l respectively. So $2l + 2b + 2(l - b) = 40$, that is $4l = 40$. We may deduce, therefore, that l is 10, but there is insufficient information for us to find the ratio $b : l$.

20. B At most one of the statements is true (as they are mutually contradictory). Indeed, the second statement is true and there is exactly one true statement.

21. D The square labelled A_1 is in the same row as C and D, the same column as E and the same diagonal as B. So it must be A. The square labelled E_2 is the next to be filled in as it is in the same row as A, C and D and in the same diagonal as B. The square labelled B_3 now completes the fourth row. The bottom left-hand corner square must now be A. This is because one of the three remaining squares in the diagonal which runs from bottom left to top right must be A, but the A at the end of row 2 means that A cannot be in either of the last two squares of this diagonal.

*				A
		B		
D	E_2	C	A_1	B_3
A_4		D_5	E	C_6

The squares D_5 and C_6 may now be filled in. We now see that the square marked * is in the same diagonal as A, B and C and in the same column as E, so it must be D. It is left as an exercise for the reader to complete the grid.

22. C The letters used in TRIANGLE are the same as those used in RECTANGLE, except that C and E have been replaced by I. So the code for TRIANGLE is $9 \times 31\,752\,000 \div (3 \times 5)$, that is $19\,051\,200$.

23. B As $XY = XZ$, $\angle XZY = \angle XYZ$, so $\angle YZW = r° - q°$. In a triangle, an exterior angle is equal to the sum of the two interior opposite angles. Applying this theorem to triangle ZYW:

$\angle ZWX = \angle YZW + \angle ZYW$, that is $p = (r - q) + r$. So $2r = p + q$.

24. C As Jack makes one revolution every five seconds, and Jill one revolution every six seconds, on average they turn through angles of $72°$ and $60°$ respectively every second. So, as they are travelling in opposite directions, Jill turns, on average, through an angle of $132°$ per second relative to Jack. In one minute, therefore, she will turn through an angle of $60 \times 132°$, that is 22 complete revolutions, relative to Jack. So they will pass each other 22 times in the first minute.

25. B Imagine the cross to consist of three horizontal layers: the first layer contains only the cube which was glued to the top face of the original cube. The second layer contains the original cube plus four additional cubes glued to the side faces of that cube. The third layer contains only the cube which was glued to the bottom face of the original cube. When yellow cubes are now added, one cube will be glued to the top face of the blue cube on the top layer and four to its side faces. Eight yellow cubes will be glued to the blue cubes in the second layer and the single blue cube in the third layer will have five yellow cubes glued to it: one to its bottom face and four to its side faces. So, overall, 18 yellow cubes are required.

JMC solutions 2006

*B A C C B * D A E E D * B C A C D * C D A D E * A B B C B*

1. **B** $6002 - 2002 = 4000$, so $6002 - 2006 = 4000 - 4 = 3996$.

2. **A** The missing numbers are A: 5, 6, 7; B: 9; C: 12, 1; D: 8, 9; E: 1, 2, 3, 4, 5. So the largest sum of numbers has been eaten on face A.

3. **C** There must be at least two boys and two girls in the family. If, for example, there was exactly one boy, then that child would not have a brother. The same argument applies to girls.

4. **C** There are 4 triangles congruent to $\triangle AQP$ (including $\triangle AQP$ itself), 2 triangles congruent to $\triangle AQB$, 2 triangles congruent to $\triangle AQD$, 4 triangles congruent to $\triangle ACD$.

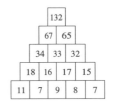

5. **B** Since 9 houses have been knocked down, $123 - 9 (= 114)$ remain.

6. **D** The completed tower is shown on the right. There is more than one order in which missing numbers may be inserted – and it is not necessary to complete the tower in order to determine n – but one possible order is 8, 17, 32, 33, 16, 7, 18, 11, 67, 132.

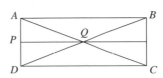

7. **A** Let the size of the reflex angle in the quadrilateral be $y°$. Then $x + y = 360$ (angles at a point). Furthermore, $35 + 15 + 25 + y = 360$ (sum of interior angles of a quadrilateral). So $x = 35 + 15 + 25$.

8. **E** Try it for yourself and see!

9. **E** $2 \times \sqrt{64} = 2 \times 8 = 16$; $22 - 2 \times 3 = 22 - 6 = 16$; $2^4 = 16$; $5^2 - 3^2 = 25 - 9 = 16$; $4 + 4 \times 2 = 4 + 8 = 12$.

10. **D** Note that you cannot remove two touching coins; for if you did then any coin making a triangle with those two coins could then slide. So if the middle coin was removed, no other coin could then be removed. So next consider removing first an outer coin. There are two outer coins touching it – which, as argued before, cannot now be removed. We consider two cases. If the next coin to go is that opposite the coin already removed, then each remaining coin is adjacent to a removed coin – and the process stops. Finally, suppose the next coin removed is next but one (around the outer edge) from the first removed coin. Then a third coin, two further around the edge, is the only possibility for removal – and then the process halts again. So the largest number of coins that may be removed is three.

11. B   The second sign is 143 miles from London and 250 miles from Edinburgh, so it is 393 miles from Edinburgh to London.

12. C   The letter 'e' already occurs eight times, so both 'nine' and 'eleven' may be placed in the gap to make the sentence true.

13. A   When divided by 7, the five options have remainder 6, 1, 3, 5, 0 respectively.

14. C   The largest and smallest possible fields of play have areas 13000 square yards and 5000 square yards respectively.

15. D   6957 is less than 7000 and 31248 is greater than 28000, so $\dfrac{6957}{31248} < \dfrac{1}{4}$. It is left as an exercise for the reader to confirm that in the other four fractions the denominator is four times the numerator.

        (Note that each of these fractions uses all the digits from 1 to 9 inclusive exactly once. The question includes the only four fractions of this type which simplify to $\frac{1}{4}$.)

16. C   The diagram shows that the regular hexagon may be divided into six congruent equilateral triangles, each of which may be further divided into four smaller congruent equilateral triangles. So the hexagon consists of 24 congruent triangles, 9 of which make up the shaded equilateral triangle.

17. D   Clearly, there must be a minimum of two 'on' switches. Two 'on' switches and three 'off' switches may be set in only one way: 'off', 'on', 'off', 'on', 'off'. Three 'on' switches and two 'off' switches may be set in six different ways. Four 'on' switches and one 'off' switch may be set in five different ways. Finally, five 'on' switches can be set in just one way. So there are 13 ways in all.

        (Note: it is left as an exercise for the reader to show that if that there are n switches then the number of different ways in which they may be set so that no two adjacent switches are in the 'off' position is the (n + 2)th term of the Fibonacci sequence 1, 1, 2, 3, 5, 8, 13, 21, 34, ...)

18. A   The total of the numbers in the magic square is 7 + 8 + 9 + ...15, that is 99. So each row, column and main diagonal has sum 33 and we deduce that the number in the top right hand corner of the square is 12. The remaining blank squares may now be completed in terms of n, as shown.

n	$21 - n$	12
$31 - 2n$	$19 - n$	7
$n + 2$	$17 - n$	14

        Considering the middle row: $31 - 2n + 19 - n + 7 = 33$, so $n = 8$.

        Alternate solution: it is known that the number in the centre of a magic square is always equal to the mean of the nine numbers making up the square, in this case 11. So $n = 33 - 14 - 11 = 8$.

19. D   After Pinocchio has told 9 lies, the length of his nose will be $2^9 \times 5$ cm
= 512×5 cm = 25.6 m. This is close to the length of a tennis court,
which is 23.8m.

20. E   As 2 is the only even prime, it must be one of the three primes which total 40
since any three odd numbers have an odd total. So the other two primes sum
to 38. Different odd numbers which total 38 are (1, 37), (3, 35), (5, 33), (7,
31), (9, 29), (11, 27), (13, 25), (15, 23), (17, 21).
Of these pairs, only (7, 31) consists of two primes, so the required difference is
24.

21. A   If the overlapping region is a triangle, two of its sides must be adjacent sides
of one of the squares. So one of its angles will be a right angle and therefore
an equilateral triangle could not appear as the overlapping region. The
diagrams show how the other options could appear as the overlapping region.

B   C   D   E

22. B   The number is 1 less than a multiple of 3, 1 less than a multiple of 4 and also
1 less than a multiple of 5. So, since 3, 4 and 5 have no factors in common, it
is 1 less than a multiple of the product of 3, 4 and 5, that is 1 less than a
multiple of 60. As it is less than 100, the only possibility is 59, which leaves
remainder 3 when divided by 7.
(*Note that the Chinese Remainder Theorem provides a general method for
solving problems like this.*)

23. B   Let the number of girls at the camp be x. Then there are $\dfrac{3x}{4}$ boys and $\dfrac{7x}{5}$
adults. So the ratio of children to adults is $\dfrac{7x}{4} : \dfrac{7x}{5}$, that is 5:4.

24. C   The total of the four triples is three times the total of the original four
numbers. So these numbers have sum $(115 + 153 + 169 + 181) \div 3$, that
is 206. Hence the largest of Amrita's numbers is $206 - 115$, that is 91.

25. B   If $\frac{1}{2}n$ is a three-digit whole number, then n is an even number between 200
and 1998 inclusive. If $2n$ is a three-digit whole number, then n is a whole
number between 50 and 499 inclusive. So for both conditions to hold, n is an
even number between 200 and 499 inclusive and there are 150 such numbers.

IMC solutions 1997

1. **D** $16 = 4 \times 4$; $36 = 6 \times 6$; $64 = 8 \times 8$ and $100 = 10 \times 10$.

2. **E** One hundred thousand and one is written as 100 001 and ten million is written as 10 000 000. Adding them gives 10 100 001

3. **B** A die has no memory. Since the die is fair the probability of a number occurring is one sixth.

4. **D** To feed 15 children needs 3 cans of soup. The 2 cans left will be enough for 6 adults.

5. **B** $\dfrac{67 \times (67 + 67)}{67} = \dfrac{67 \times 2 \times 67}{67} = \dfrac{134 \times 67}{67} = 134$.

6. **E** Since 196 is 14×14, we need something of that sort of size. The first two are definitely too small and the second two are too large.

7. **A** B is negative; D is positive but less than 1; A is 116 and C and E are both bigger.

8. **C** Something which loses all its value is reduced by 100%.

9. **D** This biggest possible product is $4 \times 5 \times 6$ but 5 and 4 are on oppsite faces and so do not share a corner. However, 3, 5 and 6 will come together as shown.

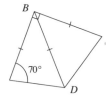

10. **E** 1 kilo is 1000g so 20g = 0.02 kilo but £1 is 100 pence so the cost is $3.41 \times 100 \times 0.02 = 341 \times 0.02$.

11. **C** Since $AB = BD$, $\triangle ABD$ is isosceles and so $\angle ADB = 70°$ from which $\angle ABD = 40°$ and hence $\angle DBC = 50°$. But $BD = BC$ and so $\angle BDC (= \angle BCD) = 65°$.

12. **D** $1 + 3 + 4 + 5 + 6 = 19$. The next multiple of 9 is 27 which is 8 more than 19.

13. **E** 2^{20} is shorthand for 20 twos multiplied together. So, that is 2×2^{19} and so half of it is 2^{19}.

14. **A** 20% of the pupils had been asked. 80% of 20% is 16%.

15. **B** After the first day, half were left. Two thirds of them, which is one third of the original, were left at the end of the second day. On the third day, one quarter left so three quarters remained and three quarters of one third is one quarter.

16. **D** In the 12 hours, Beryl covered 1.2 km more than Mike. Since 1.2 km = 1200 m, she averaged 100 m per hour more.

17. **A** The area of the square is 1 unit^2 and the area of the whole circle is $\pi \times 1^2$ units^2. So, the shaded area is $1 - \frac{1}{4}\pi$ units^2.

18. **E** $7r = 4c$ so $r < c$. $5s = 6c$ so $c < s$. Therefore $r < c < s$.

19. C The lines parallel to the x and y-axes must make a rectangle with a vertical line crossing it. To reduce the extra intersections, the sloping lines should go through as many of the existing intersections as possible. Two lines can go through two points and each of the other two through one point makin 14 points in all.

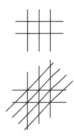

20. C Since $AD = 10$ and $BD = 8$, using Pythagoras Theorem on $\triangle ABD$ gives $AB = 6$. So, since the base of $\triangle ADC$ is 10 and its height is 6 its area must be 30.

21. B Adding the three equations gives $a + b + c = b - c + c - d + d - a$ from which $c = -2a$. Putting this into $a = b - c$ gives $b = -a$. From $b = c - d$ we get $d = c - b = -a$. Therefore,

$$\frac{a}{b} + \frac{b}{c} + \frac{c}{d} + \frac{d}{a} = -1 + \frac{1}{2} + 2 + (-1) = \frac{1}{2}.$$

22. B Since QN bisects $\angle PQR$, $\angle MQN = \angle NQR$. But, because MN and QR are parallel, $\angle MNQ = \angle NQR$. So $\angle MQN = \angle MNQ$, $\triangle MNQ$ is isosceles and therefore $MN = MQ$.

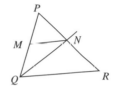

23. B Let $AB = 2x$. Then the area of each semicircle is $\frac{1}{2}\pi x^2$. But, from the square, $(2x)^2 = 1^2 + 1^2$ so $x^2 = \frac{1}{2}$ and the four semicircles total π. The shaded area is obtained by subtracting the original circle from the four semicircles plus the square, i.e. $\pi + 2 - \pi$.

24. A Each vertex lies in three faces so it can be joined to 9 vertices by face diagonals or edges. A regular dodecahedron has 20 vertices, so each vertex can be joined to 10 other vertices by space diagonals. Multiplying the number of vertices by 10 gives 200 but this counts each space diagonal twice.

25. D D4 is a two digit square:– 16, 25, 36, 49, 64 or 81. But A5 is a prime so cannot end in 5 or an even digit. A3 is a square so cannot end with 8 so D4 is 49.

A5 is prime and ends in 9:– 19, 29, 59, 79, 89. But D2 is a square so A5 is either 19 or 59. If A5 is 59 then D2 is either 225 or 625 but A1 is a prime so this fails and A5 is 19. D2 is one of 121, 361, 441 or 841 but A1 is prime so D2 is 121 or 361. The latter would give A3 as *64 which fails so D2 is 121, A3 must be 324. The top left square could be 1, 4 or 7 as all of 11, 13, 41, 43, 71 and 73 are prime.

1. 1	2. 1	
3. 3	2	4. 4
	5. 1	9

1. 4	2. 1	
3. 3	2	4. 4
	5. 1	9

1. 7	2. 1	
3. 3	2	4. 4
	5. 1	9

IMC solutions 1998

C B A A E * C C A C B * D E D D D * B D C E E * B D A A B

1. **C** One quarter of the number is 24 so the number is $4 \times 24 = 96$ and one third of 96 is 32.

2. **B** 1% of 1 is 0.01 so 6% of 6 is $0.01 \times 6 \times 6 = 0.36$ and 8% of 8 is $0.01 \times 8 \times 8 = 0.64$. Finally, $0.36 + 0.64 = 1$.

3. **A**

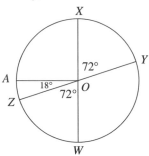

4. **A** $\dfrac{1 + 4}{7 + 4} = \dfrac{5}{11} \neq \dfrac{1}{7}$ and all the others reduce to $\dfrac{1}{7}$.

5. **E** Kevin is not in *J* or *M* but he is in *K* and *L*.

6. **C** In the diagram, the points which are equidistant from *B* and from *C* lie on the perpendicular bisector of *BC* which is the horizontal line. The points 6 cm from *A* are on the circular arc which, since $\frac{1}{2}AD = 4\frac{1}{2} < 6$, crosses the bisector of *BC* in two places.

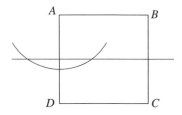

7. **C** The date of this event was 05.02.1998. $1998 = 2 \times 999 = 2 \times 9 \times 3 \times 37$ ($= 19980$). So one way is to check the years on offer for one which can be divided by 37.

Since $41 \times 37 = 1517$, we can reject 1518 and 1533.

$1665 = 45 \times 37$ which cannot be rejected.

$49 \times 37 = 1813$ which rules out 1819 and $52 \times 37 = 1924$ which rules out 1926. So Anne's birthday product is $6 \times 2 \times 1665 = 6 \times 3330 = 19980$ which is the same.

8. **A** Enlarging (or reducing) the size of a diagram does not alter the size of its angles.

9. **C** The total of all the letters is $6 + 9 + 11 + 9 + 9 = 44$. The answer in C contains 11 letters and, subtracting this from 44, leaves 33 as the number of letters in the incorrect options.

10. **B** The average was 85 so the total was $4 \times 85 = 340$. If full marks were obtained on three tests then 40 is enough on the fourth test.

11. D Number of minutes per day is $60 \times 24 = 1440$ so the number of minutes per week is $1440 \times 7 \approx 10\,000$ and the number of acres per week $\approx 54 \times 10000 \approx 500\,000$.

12. E One way of getting an answer is to try the values which are offered. Alternatively, we can set up an equation: $2C + 30 = \left(\frac{9}{5}C + 32\right) + 1$. Multiplying by 5 gives $10C + 150 = 9C + 160 + 5$ and hence $C = 165 - 150$.

13. D Since the cut is made from one edge, A and E can be rejected. C is completed the wrong shape. It cannot be B because a gutter is needed between the upper and lower halves. So we are left with D.

14. D In one hour at 90 km/hr, something would cover 90 km. In one minute, it would cover 1.5 km or 1500 m. Since 18 seconds is 0.3 of one minute, the distance the cheetah would cover would be 450 m.

The snail covers 1 km in 20 hours so would cover 50 m in 1 hour and so takes 9 hours to cover the ground covered by the cheetah in 18 seconds!

15. D

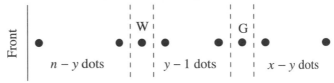

Representing each person by a dot, the information amounts to that shown above. The total number in the queue is therefore
$$(n - y) + 1 + (y - 1) + 1 + (x - y) = n + x - y + 1.$$

16. B The area of the larger tin is $12 \times 12 = 144$ square inches. Together, the area of the two smaller tins is $2 \times 8\frac{1}{2} \times 8\frac{1}{2} = \frac{1}{2} \times 17 \times 17 = \frac{1}{2} \times 289$ square inches, which is just over 144.

17. D The angles of W are $42°$, $48°$ and $90°$.
In X, $15x = 180$ so $5x = 60$ and the angles are $48°$, $60°$ and $72°$.
In Y, $8x = 180$ so $4x = 90$.
In Z, $6^2 = 36$ but $4^2 + 5^2 = 41$ so, by the Converse of Pythagoras' Theorem, it is not a right-angled triangle.

18. C The missing numbers are 1, 3, 11, 13 and 19 and d cannot be 3 or 13 or 19. Replacing the * by letters gives
$$20, a, 16, 15, 4, b, 12, c, 10, 7, 6, d, 2, 17, 14, 9, 8, 5, 18, e.$$
a cannot be 1 or 11 or 13 or 19 so it must be 3. Leaving 1, 11, 13, 19.
b cannot be 1 or 11 or 13 so it must be 19. Leaving 1, 11, 13.
c cannot be 11 or 13 so it must be 1. Leaving 11, 13.
But d is either 1 or 11 so it is 11.

19. E $z = \frac{1}{5} \times 3 \times 180 = 108$ and so $y = 180 - 108 = 72$. But, since $FA = AB$ it also equals AE and so $\triangle AFE$ is isosceles with $\angle AFE = \angle AEF = \frac{1}{2}(180 - 72)°$. Thus
$x : y : z = 54 : 72 : 108 = 3 : 4 : 6$.

20. E   Representing each edge by x cm, we know $12x = L$ and that $6x^2 = L$.
Equating these gives $12x = 6x^2$ so $x = 0$ (which is impracticable) or
$x = 2$. In this case, the volume is $2^3 = 8$ cm^3.

21. B   In the diagram, OA is one third of the altitude of the
equilateral triangle so $OA = \frac{1}{3}\sqrt{3^2 - 1\frac{1}{2}^2} = \frac{1}{3}\sqrt{\frac{27}{4}} = \sqrt{\frac{3}{4}}$
i.e. $OA = \frac{1}{2}\sqrt{3}$. So $AB^2 = 1^2 - \left(\frac{1}{2}\sqrt{3}\right)^2 = \frac{1}{4}$ which
means the sections of the triangle outside the circle
each have length 1. It also means that the parts of the
triangle inside the circle are all length 1 and thus the
triangle OBC is equilateral and each arc outside the
circle is one sixth of the circle so the three together
provide a semi-circle. So the perimeter is

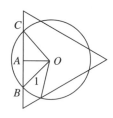

$$6 \times 1 + \tfrac{1}{2}2\pi \times 1 = 6 + \pi.$$

22. D

    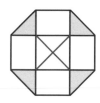

23. A   The correct place to start is A. That this might be the case can be seen as the
only triple that A could be forced to complete is the column as there is
already an O in the row and in the diagonal.

Once A has played, if the opponent plays in γ or
δ, A then plays in the other which forces the next
O to block the column. If the opponent plays in α
or β, the column is already blocked.

X	O	γ
α	X	δ
β	X	O

24. A   The diagonals of the centre square split it into four
identical right-angled triangles. The hypotenuse of each
of these triangles is 2 cm (opposite sides of a rectangle
are equal). Thus, each of these triangles is congruent to
the shaded triangles. So the four shaded triangles fit
together in the middle square and the rectangles to the
left and right match those at the top and bottom.

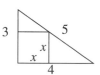

25. B   Since the triangles are similar, using x for the side of
the square allows us to equate ratios.

$$\frac{x}{4 - x} = \frac{3}{4} \Rightarrow 4x = 12 - 3x \Rightarrow x = \frac{12}{7}.$$

Thus the area of the square is $\frac{144}{49}$ and the area of the triangle is 6 so the
fraction is $\dfrac{144}{49} \div 6 = \dfrac{24}{49}$.

IMC solutions 1999

C B D E D * A E D E D * D A B E C * E C B C B * A D E A B

1.   **C**   A and B are both less than 199^2 and hence less than 199^9; $9^9 < 199^9$; $1^{999} = 1$.

2.   **B**   For B to be possible, the diagonal of a rectangle would need to be an axis of symmetry.

3.   **D**   The maximum number of days in any month is 31 and $31 \times 24 = 744$.

4.   **E**   Ima's result is ten times bigger than it should be and therefore dividing by 10 will correct her mistake. Multiplying by 0.1 is equivalent to dividing by 10.

5.   **D** $30 \div 0.2 = 300 \div 2 = 150$ or
$30 \div 0.2 = 30 \div 1/5 = 30 \times 5 = 150$.

6.   **A**   250 kg is approximately 25 times 9.6 kg. The consumption in Africa is therefore approximately 25×60, i.e. 1500, per person per year. 4 bananas per day are equivalent to 4×365, i.e. 1460, per year and the best answer is therefore A.

7.   **E**   The values are respectively ½, 1, ½, ½, ¼.

8.   **D** $\triangle PQR$ is isosceles and therefore $\angle PQR = \angle PRQ = 72°$. $\triangle PSR$ is also isosceles therefore $\angle RPS = \angle RSP = 36°$ (using the external angle theorem or by calculating that $\angle PRS = 108°$) and $x = 180° - 36° - 36° = 108°$.

9.   **E**   The ratio of height to shadow length is 1:3. Their shadow will therefore be $3 \times (1 + 1.5)$m = 7.5m long.

10.   **D**   The fine should be approximately $74 \times 52 \times 60\text{p} \approx 75 \times £30 = £2250$.

(*Historical note*: the person who returned the book disappeared without paying a fine at all!)

11.   **D**   Let the original price be £x. Then $0.8x = 60 \Rightarrow x = 60 \div 0.8 = 75$.

12.   **A**   Let the hypotenuse be of length h cm. Then $h^2 = 100 + 25 = 125$.

$$\Rightarrow h = \sqrt{125}; \; 11^2 = 121 \text{ and } 12^2 = 144 \Rightarrow 11 < h < 12$$

$$11.5^2 = (11 + \tfrac{1}{2})^2 = 11^2 + 2 \times 11 \times \tfrac{1}{2} + \tfrac{1}{4} = 132\tfrac{1}{4} \Rightarrow 11 < h < 11.5$$

$$11.25^2 = (11 + \tfrac{1}{4})^2 = 121 + 2 \times 11 \times \tfrac{1}{4} + \tfrac{1}{16}$$

$$\Rightarrow 11.25^2 > 126.5 \Rightarrow 11 < h < 11.25$$

The length of the hypotenuse is therefore closer to 11 cm than 11.5 cm.

13.   **B**   Let the radius of the circle be r. This implies that the radius of the semicircle is $2r$. The area of the semicircle is therefore $\tfrac{1}{2} \times \pi \times (2r)^2 = 2\pi r^2$ which is twice the area of the circle.

14.   **E**   The number of diagonals in an n-sided polygon is $\tfrac{1}{2}n(n - 3)$. This can be used to show that A to D are all correct. A quadrilateral has half as many diagonals as it has sides, not twice as many.

15. C   Let AB be of length $3r$. The distance moved by A is then the circumference of a semicircle of radius $3r$ i.e. $3\pi r$. C moves along the circumference of a semicircle of radius $2r$, i.e. $2\pi r$, followed by the circumference of a semicircle of radius r, i.e. πr. The total distance moved by C is therefore also $3\pi r$.

[In fact every point of the pencil moves a total distance of $3\pi r$.]

16. E   All powers of 3 are odd and $3^{10} = 3^5 \times 3^5$ which means that 3^{10} is also square.

17. C   The area of the largest circle $= 25\pi$ cm^2.
The shaded area $= (16\pi - 9\pi)$ cm$^2 = 7\pi$ cm^2.
The percentage which is shaded $= 7/25 \times 100\% = 28\%$.

18. B   Let the number of boys in Group I be x. The number of girls in Group I is therefore $40 - x$ and the number of girls in Group II is $33 - (40 - x) = x - 7$. There are therefore 7 girls fewer in Group II than there are boys in Group I.

19. C   1 wuggle = 6 waggles; 2 woggles = 5 waggles; 4 wiggles = 3 woggles = 7.5 waggles. All are therefore greater than 3 waggles.

20. B   Two murders: $2x$ hours; 6 car thefts: $6(x/6) = x$ hours; 4 bank robberies: $4(x/2) = 2x$ hours. Total $= (2x + x + 2x)$ hours $= 5x$ hours.

21. A   The product $= 3/2 \times 4/3 \times 5/4 \times 6/5 \times \ldots \times (n+1)/n$. The numerator of each fraction except the last cancels with the denominator of the next fraction, leaving $(n+1)/2$. This is equal to an integer only when n is odd.

22. D 206 – the 6 legs of the staff $= 200$. On average, at each table, there are three table legs, 16 chair legs and 6 customer legs which gives a total of 25 legs per table. $200 \div 25 = 8$, hence there are 8 tables and therefore 32 chairs.

23. E   The ten numbers in the star total 75. Each number appears in two "lines" and therefore the five "lines" total 150 which implies the sum of the numbers in each "line" is 30.
This means that $K + C = 24$ and therefore $K = 11$ and $C = 13$ or vice versa.
If $K = 11$ then $U = 12$; $I = 10$ and $M = 11$ which is impossible since $K = 11$.
If $K = 13$ then $U = 10$; $I = 12$; $M = 9$ and $C = 11$ which is correct.

24. A   The five knaves all say that a different number ate the tarts which means that only one of them can be telling the truth. K4 is the only honest knave and K1, K2, K3 and K5 ate the tarts.

25. B   The fold is made along BE. A folds onto A'.
$A'B = AB = \sqrt{2} \Rightarrow A'C = 1$ (by Pythagoras' theorem). $\triangle A'BC$ is therefore a right-angled isosceles triangle

$$\Rightarrow \angle BA'C = 45° \Rightarrow \angle EA'D = 45°$$
$$\Rightarrow ED = A'D = \sqrt{2} - 1.$$

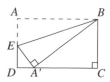

IMC solutions 2000

1. **B**   Take the units digits of any two numbers and multiply them together. The units digit of the answer is also the units digit of the product of the original two numbers. As $7 \times 9 = 63$, the units digit of 567×3489 must also be 3.

2. **A**   The angle occupied by the 'chocolate' sector is $\frac{1}{2}(360° - 90°) = 135°$. This is 1½ times bigger than the 'strawberry' sector and hence the number of chocolate ice creams sold is $1\frac{1}{2} \times 60 = 90$.

3. **E** $\frac{6}{11}$ is the only one of these fractions which is greater than $\frac{1}{2}$.

4. **C**

5. **C**   The numbers along the leading diagonal total 58 and this is therefore the sum of each row and column. We can now calculate that the number to the left of the '10' must be 20 and the number below that is 7.
Hence $x = 58 - (16 + 14 + 7) = 21$.
(A more difficult task is to calculate the value of the number in the top right-hand corner of the magic square. Can you do this?)

6. **B**   Granny dropped 4 cups and 5 saucers, leaving her with 8 cups and 5 saucers. Therefore 3 cups did not have matching saucers.

7. **D** $5^2 + 2 = 3^3$
(This is in fact the only solution of this equation for which x and y are positive whole numbers. Another way of looking at this is to say that 26 is the only whole number which is 'sandwiched' between a perfect square and a perfect cube. This was first proved by the French mathematician, Pierre de Fermat, in the 17th century.)

8. **C**   A, B and C are all equidistant from D and therefore lie on a circle whose centre is D. BC is a diameter of the circle and $\angle BAC$ is therefore the angle subtended by a diameter at a point on the circumference (the angle in a semicircle).
(Alternatively: let $\angle ACD = x$ and show that $\angle DAC = x$, $\angle ADB = 2x$ and $\angle DAB = \frac{1}{2}(180° - 2x) = 90° - x$. Hence $\angle BAC = x + 90° - x = 90°$.)

9. **B**   The numbers of multiples of 4 between 2001 and 3001 is 250. However, the following years will not be leap years: 2100, 2200, 2300, 2500, 2600, 2700, 2900, 3000. This leaves 242 leap years.

10. D   The total weight of the original five dates was 250g and the total weight of the four remaining dates was 160g.

11. D   The sale price is 75% of the original price. Therefore the amount I saved, 25% of the original price, is one third of £240, i.e. £80.

12. E   Timmy takes 24 minutes (8/20 of 1 hour) to reach the surgery; Tammy takes 18 minutes (12/40 of 1 hour) and Tommy takes 22 minutes (33/90 of 1 hour). The order, therefore, is Tammy, Tommy, Timmy.

13. B

14. D $\dfrac{b}{c} = \dfrac{a}{c} \times \dfrac{b}{a} = \dfrac{3}{4} \times \dfrac{3}{2} = \dfrac{9}{8}$.

15. C   There are 9 such numbers whose first digit is 1 : 110, 121, 132, …, 187, 198. Similarly there are 8 such numbers, beginning with 220 and ending with 297, whose first digit is 2; 7 such numbers, beginning with 330 and ending with 396, whose first digit is 3 and so on. Lastly there is only 1 such number whose first digit is 9: 990.

The answer, therefore, is $9 + 8 + 7 + 6 + 5 + 4 + 3 + 2 + 1 = 45$.

16. A   The number may be divided up into 400 blocks of '12345'. The sum of the digits in each block is 15 and hence the sum of all 2000 digits is $400 \times 15 = 6000$. Alternatively, the mean of the digits which make up the number is 3 and therefore the sum of the digits is $2000 \times 3 = 6000$.

17. D   Buying two more parsnips and three fewer turnips does not change the total cost and hence two parsnips cost the same as three turnips. Instead of six parsnips, therefore, Baldrick could have bought nine turnips and, together with seven turnips, this makes a total of sixteen turnips. Alternatively, he could have bought twelve turnips instead of the eight parsnips and, together with four turnips, this makes sixteen turnips.

18. D   We need to write $3^4 \times 4^5 \times 5^6$ in the form $a \times 10^n$ where a is not a multiple of 10.
$3^4 \times 4^5 \times 5^6 = 3^4 \times 2^{10} \times 5^6 = 3^4 \times 2^4 \times 2^6 \times 5^6 = 3^4 \times 2^4 \times 10^6$.
Hence the number ends in six zeros.

19. C   We need to express 1800 as the product of two factors, one of which (her age in months) is between twelve and thirteen times the other (her age in complete years). These are 150 and 12 respectively. Mary is 150 months old i.e. she was twelve on her last birthday and she is now 12 years 6 months old.

20. C   The percentage increases are A 25%; B 40%; C $42\frac{6}{7}$%; D 30%; E $33\frac{1}{3}$%

21. E   On the outside of the wire, the pencil describes an arc of a circle as the disc rolls around each of the corners of the triangle, but this does not happen when the disc moves around the inside of the wire.

22. C   The smallest possible number of pairs of students with the same mark will occur when every possible mark from 0 to 100 is awarded to at least one student. This accounts for 101 students and therefore the remaining 19 students must all be awarded the same mark as exactly one of their colleagues. The 120 students are made up of 19 pairs of students who are awarded the same mark and 82 students who are all awarded a different mark from everyone else.

23. B   The interior angle of a regular nine-sided polygon =
$180° - (360° ÷ 9) = 140°$. Consider the pentagon $ABCDE$:
$\angle EAB = \frac{1}{2}(540° - 3 \times 140°) = 60°$. Similarly, $\angle FAI = 60°$ and hence
$\angle FAE = 140° - (60° + 60°) = 20°$.

24. A   Let the number of ivy, nightshade and triffid plants be i, n and t respectively. Then:
$2i + 9n + 12t = 120$ and $i + n + t = 20$, where $i > 0$; $n > 0$; $t > 0$.
Multiplying the second equation by 2 and subtracting the new equation from the first:

$$7n + 10t = 80$$

$$\text{Thus } 7n = 10(8 - t)$$

Therefore n is a multiple of 10 and since $1 \leqslant n < 20, n = 10$.
Hence $8 - t = 7$ and therefore $t = 1$.

25. A   Let the large circles have radius R.
Area $A = 2 \times \pi \times \left(\frac{1}{2}R\right)^2 = \frac{1}{2}\pi R^2 \approx 1.6R^2$.
Area $B = 3 \times \frac{1}{2} \times R \times R \times \sin 120° = \frac{3}{4}\sqrt{3}R^2 \approx 1.3R^2$.
Area $C = (2R)^2 - \pi R^2 = (4 - \pi)R^2 \approx 0.9R^2$.
Area $D = 2 \times \frac{1}{2} \times R^2 = R^2$.
Area $E = \pi R^2 - \left(\sqrt{2}R\right)^2 = (\pi - 2)R^2 \approx 1.1R^2$.

IMC solutions 2001

A E A E C * D C A D B * B E B D C * B C E E D * A C B D D

1. **A**   The differences are, respectively, 11, 8, 10, 9 and 9.

2. **E**   Over a two-week period, the required number of visitors is $14 \times 30\,000 = 420\,000$. Hence the number required this week is $420\,000 - 120\,000 = 300\,000$.

3. **A**   Since $\dfrac{1}{4} = \dfrac{4}{16}$ and $\dfrac{1}{8} = \dfrac{2}{16}$, the number midway between them is $\dfrac{3}{16}$.

4. **E**   Martha has 5 children, 20 grandchildren and 60 great-grandchildren i.e. 85 descendants.

5. **C**   Angle $PSR = 41°$ (opposite angles of a parallelogram are equal). Therefore $x = 41 + 83$ because the exterior angle of a triangle is equal to the sum of the two interior opposite angles.

6. **D** $105 = 3 \times 5 \times 7$.

7. **C**   The thickness of one sheet $= (54 \div 500)$ mm $= (108 \div 1000)$ mm $= 0.108$ mm $= 0.1$ mm to one significant figure.

8. **A**   The diagram shows that triangle XYZ may be divided into 9 congruent triangles. The square $PQRS$ is made up of 4 of these 9 triangles.

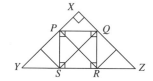

9. **D**   The number of complete days which have elapsed is $366 + 31 \approx 400$.

     Hence the number of seconds $\approx 400 \times 24 \times 60 \times 60 \approx 10000 \times 3600 = 3{\cdot}6 \times 10^7$.

10. **B**   The interior angle of a regular pentagon is $108°$. Therefore each interior angle of the regular polygon formed by the inner sides of the pentagons is $(360 - 2 \times 108)° = 144°$. The exterior angle of this regular polygon is $36°$ and hence it has $360 \div 36$, i.e. 10, sides. Therefore 7 more pentagons are required.

11. **B**   Imagine that the card is transparent. Then, after the first rotation the shape on the card will look like и. The diagonal line now runs North-East to South West and so it will appear the same after the second rotation. The line which runs North-South on the left of the figure will run East-West at the bottom of the figure after this second rotation, while the line which runs North-South on the right of the figure will run East-West at the top of the figure. Thus the final appearance will be ⊒.

12. E   Every long-sleeve shirt requires 2 cuff buttons; hence for every one long-sleeve shirt produced by the factory, a total of 20 front buttons are used. The long-sleeve shirt requires 8 of these and therefore the remaining 12 will be the front buttons on 2 short-sleeve shirts. Thus the required ratio is 1:2.

13. B   The general form of the example given is
$1 + 3 + 5 + \ldots + (2n - 1) + \ldots + 5 + 3 + 1 = (n - 1)^2 + n^2$. Therefore, for $n = 1001$:

$$1 + 3 + 5 + \ldots + 1999 + 2001 + 1999 + \ldots + 5 + 3 + 1 = 1000^2 + 1001^2.$$

14. D   The only possible distinct patterns are:

15. C $3\sqrt{11} = \sqrt{9} \times \sqrt{11} = \sqrt{9 \times 11} = \sqrt{99}$; similarly, $4\sqrt{7} = \sqrt{112}$; $5\sqrt{5} = \sqrt{125}$; $6\sqrt{3} = \sqrt{108}$; $7\sqrt{2} = \sqrt{98}$. Hence $4\sqrt{7}$, $5\sqrt{5}$ and $6\sqrt{3}$ are all greater than 10.

16. B   One cake and one bun cost a total of 62p. Note that $512 \div 62 = 8$ remainder 16 and note also that $16 = 39 - 23$. Hence
$512 = 8(39 + 23) + 16 = 8(39 + 23) + 39 - 23 = 9 \times 39 + 7 \times 23$.
As 39 and 23 do not have a common factor, other than 1, Helen must have bought 9 cakes and 7 buns.

17. C   In each minute, the two clocks showed the same time for 40 seconds i.e. they showed the same time for $\dfrac{40}{60}$ of the day.

18. E   Let the athlete take x minutes to cycle one mile. Then he takes $\frac{3x}{2}$ minutes to run one mile, and $3x$ minutes to walk one mile. Therefore:
$3x + \frac{3x}{2} + x = 3x + 10$ i.e. $x = 4$.
The cyclist takes 12 minutes to walk the first mile, 6 minutes to run the second mile and 4 minutes to cycle the third mile: a total time of 22 minutes.

19. E   The ratio length:breadth of the smaller rectangles is 5:4. Let the length and breadth of these rectangles be $5x$ cm and $4x$ cm respectively. The area of the large rectangle, in cm^2, is $9 \times 20x^2 = 180x^2$ and the only one of the alternatives which is a product of 180 and a perfect square is 1620, which corresponds to $x = 3$.

20. D   Note that the sum of the whole numbers from 1 to 9 inclusive is 45, a multiple of 3. Thus the stated problem may be reduced to finding the number of ways of choosing two of these numbers whose sum is a multiple of 3. There are 12 ways of doing this: 1, 2; 1, 5; 1, 8; 2, 4; 2, 7; 3, 6; 3, 9; 4, 5; 4, 8; 5, 7; 6, 9; 7, 8.

21. A   Given that $0 < x < 1$, we may deduce that $x^2 + x > x^2 > x^3 > x^4$ and also that $x^2 + x > x^2 + x^3$.

22. C   For the triangular faces of the resulting solid to be equilateral, it is necessary for each of the solids removed at the corners to be a regular tetrahedron. Removing a regular tetrahedron at a corner in this manner does not change the total length of the edges of the solid as the perimeter of the equilateral triangle created is equal to the sum of the other three edges of the removed tetrahedron. The original tetrahedron had six edges, all of side 6 cm, and therefore the total length of the edges of the resulting solid is 36 cm.

23. B   Note that $\dfrac{n+3}{n-1} = \dfrac{n-1}{n-1} + \dfrac{4}{n-1} = 1 + \dfrac{4}{n-1}$. Thus $\dfrac{n+3}{n-1}$ is an integer if and only if $n-1$ divides exactly into 4 (or -4). The values of n for which this is true are $-3, -1, 0, 2, 3$ and 5.

24. D   The totals of the top row and the completed main diagonal are 30 and 39 respectively and therefore the ten consecutive numbers in question must be those from 30 to 39 inclusive. The number in the bottom right-hand corner must be one of 1, 2, 8, 15 or 16. Taking 1 or 2 makes the diagonal (from top left to bottom right) add up to less than 30, while taking 15 or 16 produces a total greater than 39. Hence 8 must go in the bottom right-hand corner. It now follows that * must be replaced by 15, since if 15 is placed in one of the other three vacant squares, we get a total of 45 (second column, too big), 34 (third column, same as diagonal) or 47 (third row, too big). You should check that the square can now be completed successfully.

25. D   Let O be the centre of the circle and let the points where the arcs meet be C and D respectively. $ABCD$ is a square since its sides are all equal to the radius of the arc CD and $\angle ACB = 90°$ (angle in a semicircle).

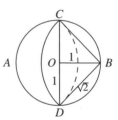

In triangle OCB, $CB^2 = OC^2 + OB^2$; hence $CB = \sqrt{2}$ cm. The area of the segment bounded by arc CD and diameter CD is equal to the area of sector BCD – the area of triangle BCD, i.e. $\left(\dfrac{1}{4}\pi\left(\sqrt{2}\right)^2 - \dfrac{1}{2} \times \sqrt{2} \times \sqrt{2}\right)$ cm^2 i.e. $\left(\tfrac{1}{2}\pi - 1\right)$ cm^2.

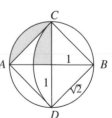

The unshaded area in the original figure is, therefore, $(\pi - 2)$ cm^2. Now the area of the circle is π cm^2 and hence the shaded area is 2 cm^2.

(Note that the shaded area is equal to the area of square ABCD. This can be proved by showing that the areas of the two regions shaded in the lower diagram are equal. This is left as a task for the reader.)

IMC solutions 2002

*D D C B E * C B D B C * D A E E D * C B A A A * D C E C B*

1. **D** $3 = \dfrac{15}{5}$ and $4 = \dfrac{20}{5}$; 19 is the only one of the options between 15 and 20.

2. **D** $0.3 \times 7 = 2.1$; $0.5 \times 5 = 2.5$; $0.2 \times 11 = 2.2$; $0.09 \times 30 = 2.7$ and $0.026 \times 100 = 2.6$.

3. **C**   When 17 is divided by 3, there is a remainder of 2. Thus there are either 2 chairs, 5 chairs, or more. Since 5 chairs have too many legs there must be 2 chairs and 3 stools.

4. **B**   Taking the altitude shown, symmetry can be obtained by shading 3 more triangles. Taking the vertical altitude would require 5 more to be shaded and the other sloping altitude would need 6 more.

5. **E**   The cost for 9 apples would be $(24 + 23 + \ldots + 16) = 180$ pence.

6. **C** $6 \times 3 = 18$; $7 \times 5 = 35$; $8 \times 5 = 40$; $9 \times 4 = 36$; $10 \times 3 = 30$.

7. **B**   The diagram shows that the required area is made up of six congruent triangles. Thus the area, in m², is $6 \times (\tfrac{1}{2} \times 6 \times 3) = 6 \times 9$.

8. **D** $2^{10} = 2 \times 2 \times 2 \times 2 \times 2 \times 2 \times 2 \times 2 \times 2 \times 2 = 1024$. So the answer comes from $1024 - 100$.

9. **B**   A has adjacent 3s. In C, the 3s are just one digit apart. In D, the 3s are just two digits apart. In E, the 4s are adjacent. But B satisfies all the requirements.

10. **C**   In the family, there are 3 boys and 6 girls. So Tom has 2 brothers and 6 sisters.

11. **D**   Let the first term be x. Then the sequence is: x, 4, $x + 4$, $x + 8$, $2x + 12$. So $2x + 12 = 22$ and hence $x = 5$.

12. **A**   Along the bottom, there is a pair of black counters which is a threat to the second player. If Black plays at D then White can play at A *but* if Black plays at A then White is helpless. If Black plays at E, White can play at C and vice versa. If Black plays at B, then White can play to the right of B, blocking that row.

13. **E**   The guesses were 5040, 5060, 5110, 5120, 5150. The range of these guesses

is just 110 so the two 'wild' estimates must both be low or both high. Since the difference between 5040 and 5060 is 20, 5040 is 90 out and 5060 is 70 out.

14. E By the Theorem of Pythagoras, the diagonal of the window is 100cm which exceeds the length or the breadth of all the sheets. So the first three pieces can go through the window either way and the 90 cm × 105 cm piece can also go through the window provided that a 90 cm edge goes first.

15. D

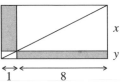

The sequence of cards I am given is a, c, e, d, b. This gives a = Ace; c = 2; e = 3; d = 4; b = 5. Hence the original order was Ace, 5, 2, 4, 3.

16. C The two angles marked $y°$ are equal because they are in an isosceles triangle. For the same reason, the angles $z°$ are equal. Since an exterior angle of a triangle is the sum of the two interior and opposite angles, it follows that $a = 2y$ and $b = 2z$. Now $a° + b° = 180°$ since they are the base angles of a parallelogram. So $2y + 2z = 180$ giving $y + z = 90$. But, from the angle sum of a triangle, $x + y + z = 180$; hence $x = 90$.

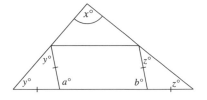

17. B Let the distance to the bike shop be d miles. Then the time going is $\frac{1}{3}d$ hours and the time returning is $\frac{1}{12}d$ hours. The total travelling time is thus $\frac{1}{3}d + \frac{1}{12}d = \frac{5}{12}d$ hours and the total distance is $2d$ miles giving the average speed as $(2d) \div (\frac{5}{12}d) = 2 \times \frac{12}{5} = \frac{24}{5}$ miles per hour.

18. A

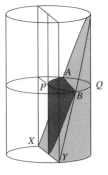

Let x and y be the distances shown. Then the shaded area is $8y + x$. But there are a number of similar triangles and from one pair $\frac{x}{8} = \frac{y}{1}$ i.e. $x = 8y$. So,

$$\frac{\text{shaded area}}{\text{total area}} = \frac{8y + x}{9(x + y)} = \frac{8y + 8y}{9 \times 9y} = \frac{16}{81}.$$

19. A Imagine the liquid became solidified. Rotate the can until the face which contains XY is horizontal.

Now take the horizontal cross-section half way up the can which meets the plane face of the 'liquid' in the line AB. Observing that AB bisects the radius PQ, rotate the upper section of the 'liquid' about AB through 180°. The new position is shaded darkly and fits into the bottom right quarter (with some space to spare).

[The actual fraction can be shown to be $2/(3\pi)$, i.e. approximately 0.21.]

20. A The maximum score is 135. If a candidate omits one of the first 15 questions, or answers it wrongly, then effectively 5 marks are lost from a possible maximum score. Similarly, if one of questions 16 to 25 is omitted then effectively 6 marks are lost. If one of questions 16 to 20 is answered incorrectly then effectively 7 marks are lost and an incorrect answer to one of questions 21 to 25 effectively loses 8 marks. Thus scores of 130, 129, 128 and 127 are all possible but 126 is not possible since one omission or incorrect answer effectively loses a maximum of 8 marks, while two omissions or incorrect answers lead to an effective loss of at least 10 marks.

21. D

Year	2002	2003	2004	2005	2006	2007	2008
1st January	Tu	Wed	Thu	Sat	Sun	Mon	Tue
	2009	2010	2011	2012	2013	2014	
	Thu	Fri	Sat	Sun	Tue	Wed	

So two years in the list start on a Tuesday. But *each* date has to fall on the same day and since 2008 is a leap year, it must be excluded.

22. C By extending the short sides, one can construct another triangle. Since all the angles involved are $60°$, the new small triangles and the new large triangle are all equilateral. The sides of the new, large triangle are
$13 + 3 + 11 = 11 + 6 + 10 = 10 + 4 + 13 = 27.$

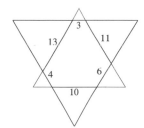

23. E The description does not say that the heptagon has to be convex, i.e. all of its interior angles need not be less than $180°$. Since $(2 \times 7 - 4) \times 90 = 900$ the interior angles of all heptagons total $900°$. The creation of a heptagon with all the given conditions is possible as the diagram shows. Notice that four of the interior angles are acute and the other three are *reflex* angles.

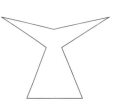

24. C To satisfy the stated condition, the display will have the form $10:m_1m_2:s_1s_2$. The values of both m_1 and s_1 have to be chosen from 2, 3, 4, 5. So there are four ways of choosing m_1 and then three choices for s_1. Since four digits have been chosen, m_2 and s_2 are selected from the remaining six. Thus the total number of times is $4 \times 3 \times 6 \times 5 = 360$.

25. B $x = 1 - \dfrac{1}{111111} = 1 - \dfrac{6}{666666}; y = 1 - \dfrac{2}{222223} = 1 - \dfrac{6}{666669};$
$z = 1 - \dfrac{3}{333334} = 1 - \dfrac{6}{666668}.$ Now $\dfrac{6}{666669} < \dfrac{6}{666668} < \dfrac{6}{666666}$
and so $x < z < y$.

IMC solutions 2003

E D A C E * *D C D E C* * *B B C A E* * *C A E B D* * *D C A B A*

1. **E** $3 \div \frac{1}{2} = 3 \times 2 = 6$.

2. **D** The words are MILE and YARD.

3. **A** $643566 \div 2786 = 231$ so $643566 \div 27.86 = 231 \times 100 = 23100$.

4. **C** One mile is approximately equal to 1.6 kilometres so 120 miles are approximately equal to 200 kilometres.

5. **E** $(2000 + 3)^2 = 2000^2 + 2 \times 2000 \times 3 + 3^2 = 4\,000\,000 + 12\,000 + 9 = 4\,012\,009$.

6. **D** Let the number thought of be x. Then the final number is $4(2x + 3) - 5 - x = 7x + 7 = 7(x + 1)$.

7. **C** The transfer fee for a total of 12 players would be three times that for 4 players.

8. **D** Angle $BCD = x$ (vertically opposite angles);
Angle BDC = angle BCD
                (base angles of isosceles triangle);
Angle ABC = angle BCD (alternate angles);
Angle EBD = angle BDC (alternate angles).

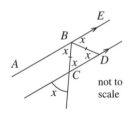

not to scale

9. **E** 60 million × 70 kg = 4 200 million kg = 4.2 million tonnes, since 1 tonne = 1000 kg.

10. **C** The digits will next be all the same at 11.11, i.e. in 5 hours and 16 minutes time.

11. **B** The fractions exceed $\frac{1}{2}$ by $\frac{1}{14}, \frac{1}{8}, \frac{1}{4}, \frac{3}{22}$ and $\frac{3}{26}$ respectively i.e. by $\frac{3}{42}, \frac{3}{24}, \frac{3}{12}, \frac{3}{22}$ and $\frac{3}{26}$. Thus the fraction in the middle will be that which exceeds $\frac{1}{2}$ by $\frac{3}{24}$.
[*Alternatively, when the fractions are written as decimals, correct to 3 decimal places, their values are 0.571, 0.625, 0.75, 0.636 and 0.615 respectively.*]

12. **B** Each edge of the cube borders two faces. As there are 6 faces, a minimum of three black edges will be required. The diagram shows that the required condition may indeed be satisfied with three black edges.

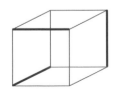

13. C   The diagram shows that it is possible to fit five T shapes in the square. In order to fit six T shapes into the square, exactly one of the 25 squares would be left uncovered; hence at least three corner squares must be covered.

We now label a corner square *H* or *V* if it is covered by a T shape which has the top part of the T horizontal or vertical respectively. If all four corner squares are covered then there must be at least two cases of an *H* corner with an adjacent *V* corner. Each such combination produces a non-corner square which cannot be covered e.g. the second square from the 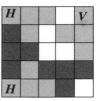 right on the top row of the diagram. If only three corner squares are covered, there must again be at least one *H* corner with an adjacent V corner and therefore a non-corner square uncovered, as well as the uncovered fourth corner. In both cases, at least two squares are uncovered, which means that it is impossible to fit six T shapes into the square.

14. A   As *OQ* is the reflection of *OP* in *OM*, $\angle QOM = \angle POM$; similarly, $\angle RON = \angle PON$. Hence reflex $\angle QOR = 2 \times \angle MON = 260°$. Therefore $\angle QOR = 360° - 260° = 100°$.

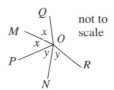

15. E   As each interior angle of the polygon is a whole number of degrees, the same must apply to each exterior angle. The sum of the exterior angles of a polygon is 360° and so the greatest number of sides will be that of a 360-sided polygon in which each interior angle is 179°, thus making each exterior angle 1°.

16. C   Minnie's average speed this year is $\frac{5}{4}$ of last year's value. Hence her time this year will be $\frac{4}{5}$, i.e. 80%, of last year's time.

17. A   The shaded area may be divided into a 2 × 1 rectangle plus a semicircle and two quarter circles, all of radius 1. Hence the total area is that of the rectangle plus that of a circle of radius 1 i.e. $2 + \pi$.

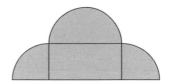

18. E   All palindromic dates this century will fall in February as they will be of the form *ab* 02 20*ba*. The palindromic dates next century will fall in December as they will be of the form *cd* 12 21*dc* and the first of these will be the 10th of December 2101 i.e. 10 12 2101.

19. B   The area of the pentagon is that of a rectangle of length *b* and breadth *a* plus that of a triangle of base *b* and height $(c - a)$ i.e. $ab + \frac{1}{2}b(c - a) = \frac{1}{2}b(2a + c - a) = \frac{1}{2}b(a + c)$.

[The area may also be considered to be the sum of the areas of two trapezia which have parallel sides *a* and *c* and whose heights have total length *b*.]

20. D We are given that $2n + e = 8$ and $t + e + n = 10$. Subtracting the first equation from the second gives $t - n = 2$. As n cannot equal 1, the minimum value of t is 4 but this gives $n = 2$, $e = 4$ which is impossible. If $t = 5$ then $n = 3$ and $e = 2$, which is allowed. If $t > 5$ then $n > 3$ and e is not a positive whole number, so 5 is the only possible value of t.

21. D Let the radius of R's track be r and let the radius of the first semicircle of P's track be p; then the radius of the second semicircle of this track is $r - p$. The total length of P's track is $\pi p + \pi(r - p) = \pi r$, the same as the length of R's track. By a similar argument, the length of Q's track is also πr, so all three runners finish at the same time.

22. C Each side of the dodecagon subtends an angle of 30° at the centre of the circumcircle of the figure (the circle which passes through all 12 of its vertices). Thus $\angle AOB = 150°$ and, as the angle subtended by an arc at the centre of a circle is twice the angle subtended by that arc at a point on the circumference, $\angle APB = 75°$.

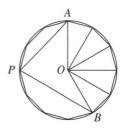

23. A It takes ab man-hours to paint c square metres of the bridge and hence $\dfrac{ab}{c}$ man-hours to paint 1 square metre. So d men will take $\dfrac{ab}{cd}$ hours to paint 1 square metre and $\dfrac{abe}{cd}$ hours to paint e square metres.

24. B The figure shows the top left-hand corner of the complete diagram and we see by symmetry that the perpendicular from the corner to the short side of the rectangle has length $\frac{1}{2}$. Thus the diagonal of the square may be divided into three sections of length $\frac{1}{2}$, x and $\frac{1}{2}$ respectively.

The length of this diagonal $= \sqrt{10^2 + 10^2} = \sqrt{200} = 10\sqrt{2}$, so $x = 10\sqrt{2} - 1$.

25. A Let the widescreen width and traditional width be w and W respectively. Then the respective heights are $\dfrac{9w}{16}$ and $\dfrac{3W}{4}$. As the areas are equal:

$$w \times \frac{9w}{16} = W \times \frac{3W}{4} \text{ i.e. } w^2 = \tfrac{4}{3}W^2. \text{ Hence } w : W = 2 : \sqrt{3}.$$

IMC solutions 2004

$D E E C B * B D D E E * A A C B D * C B E D C * D A C A B$

1. **D** $4004 - 2004 = 2000$, so $4002 - 2004 = 2000 - 2 = 1998$.

2. **E**   There must be 25 pupils who all have different birthdays. If the remaining 5 pupils all have the same birthday as one of these pupils, then 6 pupils will share the same birthday.

3. **E** $37\ 373 + 61\ 392 = 98\ 765$ and $45\ 678 + 53\ 087 = 98\ 765$.

4. **C**   The angles marked $a°$, $c°$ and $e°$ may be considered to be the exterior angles of the triangle and therefore have a total of $360°$. As $b° = a°, d° = c°$ and $f° = e°$ (all pairs of vertically opposite angles), $b + d + f = 360$. So $a + b + c + d + e + f = 720$.

5. **B**   Let the numbers be x and y. Then $x + y = 2; x - y = 4$. Adding these equations gives $2x = 6$, so $x = 3$. Hence $y = 2 - 3 = -1$ so the numbers are 3 and -1.

6. **B**   The sum is what we would write as $162 + 257$ and this equals 419. However, in Niatirb it would be written 580.

7. **D**   The shaded area is a trapezium of area $\frac{1}{2}(3 + 7) \times 5 = 25$. Line XD forms one side of a trapezium of area 12.5, since $\frac{1}{2}(1 + 4) \times 5 = 12.5$.

8. **D**   The average number of rubber bands added each day was approximately $\frac{6\ 000\ 000}{5 \times 365} \approx \frac{6\ 000\ 000}{1800} \approx 3300$.

9. **E**   The surface areas of the cuboids are: A 68; B 70; C 56; D 52; E 76.

10. **E**   The four fractions total $\frac{5}{4}$, so their mean $= \frac{5}{4} \div 4 = \frac{5}{16}$.

11. **A**   The 49 black squares will be in a 7×7 formation, so the board will measure 15×15 squares. Hence the number of white squares $= 225 - 49 = 176$.

12. **A**   As the diagram shows, the figure may be cut into two parts which fit together to form a square measuring 8cm × 8cm.

13. **C**   Points $(-3, -3)$, $(-2, -1)$, $(4, 11)$ and $(5, 13)$ all lie on the line whose equation is $y = 2x + 3$, but $(2, 5)$ does not lie on this line.

14. **B**   We note first that $y = 5$ since that is the only non-zero digit which, when it is multiplied by 3, has itself as the units digit. So there is a carry of 1 into the tens column. We note also that $a = 1$ or $a = 2$ as "*fly*" < 1000 and therefore $3 \times$ "*fly*" < 3000. We now need $3 \times l + 1$ to end in either 1 or 2 and the only possibility is $l = 7$, giving $a = 2$ with a carry of 2 into the hundreds column. As $a = 2, f$ must be at least 6. However, if $f = 6$ then $w = 0$ which is not allowed. Also the letters represent different digits, so $f \neq 7$ and we can also deduce that $f \neq 9$ since $f = 9$ would make $w = 9$.
Hence $f = 8$, making $w = 6$ and the letters represent $875 \times 3 = 2625$.

15. D As triangle A has two equal sides, it should have two equal angles, but its angles are 25°, 110° and 45° so it is impossible to make. In a triangle, the smallest angle lies opposite the shortest side which makes B impossible since 20° is the smallest angle, but 5 cm is not the shortest side. Triangle C is impossible as $4^2 + 7^2 \neq 8^2$, so it does not obey Pythagoras' Theorem. The longest side of a triangle must be shorter than the sum of the other two sides, but this is not the case in triangle E, so it cannot be made either. Triangle D, however, is obtained by cutting an equilateral triangle of side 6cm in half along an axis of symmetry and so can certainly be made.

16. C Note that the number at the end of the n th row is n^2, so 400 will lie at the end of the 20 th row. The row below will end in 21^2, i.e. 441, so the number directly below 400 will be 440.

17. B As P and Q both lie between 0 and 1, their product will be greater than 0 but smaller than P and smaller than Q. Of the options available, only B satisfies these conditions. (Furthermore, its position is correct since P is approximately equal to $\frac{1}{2}$, which means that the product of P and Q lies approximately half way between 0 and Q.)

18. E Angle $PRS = 30°$, so triangle PRS is isosceles with $SP = SR$.

Hence $\dfrac{QS}{SR} = \dfrac{QS}{SP} = \dfrac{1}{2}$ as PQS is half of an equilateral triangle.

[Alternatively, we can use the angle bisector theorem: $\dfrac{QS}{SR} = \dfrac{PQ}{PR} = \dfrac{1}{2}$ as PQR is also half of an equilateral triangle.]

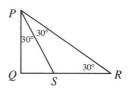

19. D Consider the cuboid to be made up of 60 unit cubes. The front and side views show that top and bottom layers consist of the same number of cubes and from the top view we see that this number is 14. The front and side views indicate that only the 4 corner cubes remain in the middle layer, so the total number of cubes remaining is $2 \times 14 + 4 = 32$. The required fraction, therefore, is $\dfrac{32}{60} = \dfrac{8}{15}$.

20. C Using the formula for the difference of two squares: $127^2 - 1 = 127^2 - 1^2 = (127 + 1)(127 - 1) = 128 \times 126 = 2^7 \times 2 \times 63 = 2^8 \times 3^2 \times 7$.

21. D Let the length of a short side of a rectangle be x and the length of a long side be y. Then the whole square has side of length $(y + x)$, whilst the small square has side of length $(y - x)$. As the area of the whole square is four times the area of the small square, the length of the side of the whole square is twice the length of the side of the small square. Therefore $y + x = 2(y - x)$ i.e. $y = 3x$ so $x : y = 1 : 3$.

22. A If you answer all questions correctly, you receive m marks for each of the N questions plus an extra 2 marks for the last $(N - q)$ questions. So the maximum possible score $= m \times N + 2 \times (N - q) = mN + 2N - 2q$
$= (m + 2)N - 2q$.

23. C Let the centres of the circles be J and O and let NI be the common tangent shown. Let P be the point of intersection of JO and LM. As arc KL is 5/8 of the circumference of the top circle, $\angle IJL = 45°$. Consider quadrilateral $IJON$: sides IJ and NO are radii, so they are both of unit length and they are both perpendicular to tangent NI. So $IJON$ is a rectangle. Hence $\angle IJO = 90°$ and $\angle LJP = 90° - 45° = 45°$. In triangle JLP, $\angle JPL = 180° - (90° + 45°) = 45°$. So triangle JLP is isosceles and $LP = LJ = 1$ unit.

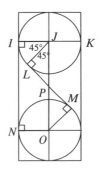

By a similar argument, it may be shown that PM is also of length 1 unit, so $LM = LP + PM = 2$ units.

24. A We may deduce that $p > q$, so, as p and q are both positive, $\dfrac{p^2}{q^2} > \dfrac{\sqrt{p}}{\sqrt{q}} > 1$.

We may also deduce that $0 < \dfrac{q^2}{p^2} < \dfrac{q}{p} < \dfrac{\sqrt{q}}{\sqrt{p}} < 1$ and hence $\dfrac{q^2}{p^2}$ is the least of the five numbers.

25. B Triangles ABG, GFE and EFA are similar, so $AF : FE = EF : FG = GB : BA = 1 : 2$. Thus if $AF = a$, then $FE = 2a$, $FG = 4a$, and the shaded area is $8a^2$. By Pythagoras' Theorem, $AE = \sqrt{5}a$, so $AD = 2\sqrt{5}a$ and the area of the square is $20a^2$. Thus the required fraction is $8 / 20$, which is $2 / 5$.

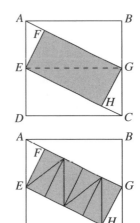

[Alternatively, as we have shown that $FG = 4AF$, we can divide parallelogram $AGCE$ into 10 congruent triangles, 8 of which make up rectangle $EFGH$. So the area of the rectangle is 4/5 of the area of the parallelogram, which in turn is half the area of square $ABCD$.]

IMC solutions 2005

*E D A B C * D B A D C * C B D C A * B C E C D * E A E A B*

1. **E** In increasing order, the numbers are 4.004, 4.04, 4.044, 4.4, 4.44.

2. **D** 10% of one million is 100 000; 10% of one thousand is 100; 100 000 − 100 = 99 900.

3. **A** As the hands move anticlockwise, at 1:30 pm they would have the appearance they would normally have at 10:30. So, as the clock is viewed in a mirror, it would have the appearance shown in A.

4. **B** The values of the expressions are, respectively, 202, 2005, 9010, 27 217 and 65 026.

5. **C** If a number is divisible by 6 then it must also be divisible by 2, so is even. 'The sum of any two odd numbers is even' is also true. However, not all multiples of 9 are odd (e.g. 18) and the sum of any two even numbers is even rather than odd, so two of the four statements are true.

6. **D** The offer gives the purchaser two items for the price of one and a half items. So the average cost per item is the same as four items for the price of three.

7. **B** Let the sizes of the interior angles of the quadrilateral in the centre of the figure be $a°$, $b°$, $c°$ and $d°$. Then $a + b + c + d = 360$. Each of these angles is vertically opposite to one of the unmarked angles in the four triangles, as shown. So the sum of the marked angles plus the four angles of the quadrilateral is equal to the sum of the interior angles of four triangles, that is 720°. Hence the sum of the marked angles is $720° − 360° = 360°$.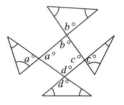

8. **A** The required fraction = $\dfrac{6\frac{3}{4}}{24} = \dfrac{27}{96} = \dfrac{9}{32}$.

9. **D** The area of triangle A = $\frac{1}{2} \times 2 \times 3 = 3$; the area of parallelogram B = $1 \times 3 = 3$; the area of triangle C = $\frac{1}{2} \times 3 \times 2 = 3$; the area of rectangle E = $1 \times 3 = 3$. However, the area of triangle D = $3 \times 3 − (3 + 3 + \frac{1}{2}) = 2\frac{1}{2}$.

10. **C** Let the weights in kg of the head and body of the fish be h and b respectively. Then $h = 9 + \frac{1}{3}b$ and $b = h + 9$. So $b = 9 + \frac{1}{3}b + 9$, that is $\frac{2}{3}b = 18$, which gives $b = 27$. Hence $h = 18$, so the whole fish weighed 54kg.

11. **C** The side of length 5cm cannot be the hypotenuse of the right-angled triangle as it is shorter than the side of length 6cm. If the 6cm side is the hypotenuse, then the third side of the triangle has length $\sqrt{11}$ cm. If the 6cm side is not the hypotenuse, then the hypotenuse has length $\sqrt{61}$ cm. These are the only two possibilities.

12. B   Ten gallons of honey would provide enough fuel for one bee to fly about 70 000 000 miles. So the number of bees which could fly 1000 miles is approximately 70 000 000 ÷ 1000, that is 70 000.

13. D   Considering the angles at B and E:
$\angle CBE = (180 - 75 - 60)° = 45°$;
$\angle DEB = (180 - 65 - 60)° = 55°$. Therefore
$\angle GHB = (45 + 55)° = 100°$ (exterior angle theorem) and, using the same theorem,
$\angle HGC = (100 - 60)° = 40°$.

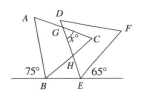

14. C   Let $ABCD$ be the cross-section of one of the stones, as shown. As $AD = BC$, $ABCD$ is an isosceles trapezium with $\angle ADC = \angle BCD$ (the proof of which is left to the reader). If $\angle ADC = \angle BCD = \theta$, then 2θ is the interior angle of a regular 20-sided polygon, namely $(180 - 360/20)°$, which equals $162°$. So θ is $81°$.

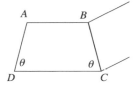

15. A   Four bags of porridge contain one-fifth of a bag of wheatbran. So the proportion of wheatbran in the porridge is 1/20, that is 5%.

16. B   The two dark squares are those on which the block stands originally. After the first move, it occupies the squares labelled '1' or '1/5'. After the second move it occupies the squares labelled '2' and so on. After the fifth and final move, it occupies the squares labelled '5' or '1/5'.

As can be seen, 19 squares are occupied altogether.

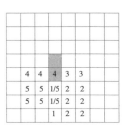

17. C   The volume of 1kg of platinum is $(1000/21.45)\text{cm}^3$, that is approximately 50 cm^3. So 1 tonne of platinum has a volume of approximately 50 000cm^3, which is $1/20\text{m}^3$. The volume of platinum produced per year is therefore about 5m^3 and the total volume of platinum ever produced is approximately 250m^3. This is the volume of a cuboid measuring 10m × 5m × 5m, which is comparable to a house.

18. E   The area of the rectangle is 48cm^2, so the unshaded area is 12cm^2. Therefore $\frac{1}{2} \times x \times 2 + \frac{1}{2} \times (6 - x) \times 8 = 12$, that is $x + 24 - 4x = 12$, so $x = 4$.

19. C   For ease of reference, label the points $A, B, C, \ldots, K$ as
shown.

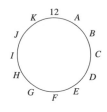

First note that $A = 3$ and $K = 9$ or vice versa. With no
loss of generality, let $A = 3$. Then the only possible
values for B, C and D are 7, 8 and 2 respectively. This
gives $E = 1$ or 4 and, as $K = 9$, $J = 1$ or 6. If $J = 1$,
then $E = 4$ and the only remaining possibilities for I, H
and G are 5, 10 and 11 respectively. This means that
$F = 6$, but $11 + 6$ is not a triangle number, so J is not 1 and must, therefore,
be 6. This means that $I = 4$ and hence $E = 1$. The remaining values may now
be assigned: $H = 11, G = 10$ and $F = 5$.

20. D   The mean of the nine consecutive positive integers is the fifth of the
numbers, so their sum is nine times the fifth number. As nine is itself a
perfect square, the sum will be a perfect square if and only if the fifth number
is a perfect square. For the options given, the fifth numbers are 114, 124,
134, 144 and 154 respectively.

21. E   The diagram shows points A and B, which are the
centres of the two circles, and C, the point on BQ
such that AC is parallel to PQ. As radii PA and QB
are both perpendicular to tangent PQ, $APQC$ is a
rectangle. So $\angle ACB$ is a right angle. The length of
$AB = 1 + 4 = 5$; the length of $BC = 4 - 1 = 3$. So, by
Pythagoras' Theorem, $AC = \sqrt{5^2 - 3^2} = 4$, which,
therefore, is also the length of PQ.

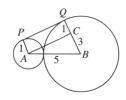

22. A   Let the number of cases solved in 2003 be x. Then, as this was 80% of the
number of cases, there were $5x/4$ cases to solve in 2003. So the number of
cases to solve in 2004 was $5x/4 \times 6/5$, which is $3x/2$. Inspector Remorse
solved 60% of these cases, that is $3x/2 \times 3/5$, which is $9x/10$. So the
change in the number of cases solved was a 10% decrease.

23. E   The equations of the three lines must be considered in pairs to find the
coordinates of their points of intersection, i.e. the coordinates of the vertices
of the triangle. It is left to the reader to show that these are $(-15, -9)$, $(0, 6)$
and $(5, 1)$. The area of the triangle may now be found by enclosing it in a
rectangle measuring 20×15 and subtracting the areas of the three
surrounding triangles from that of the rectangle. This gives
$300 - (112\frac{1}{2} + 12\frac{1}{2} + 100) = 75$.

24. A   Figure (i) shows a net of the cube on which a possible path has been drawn, while figure (ii) shows a diagram of the cube on which the same path has been drawn. Each edge of the network which joins a corner to a face centre has length $1/\sqrt{2}$, while each edge which joins two adjacent corners has length 1. So the length of the path shown is $1 + 12 \times 1/\sqrt{2}$, that is $1 + 6\sqrt{2}$. This is the length of the shortest path along the edges of the network which passes through all 14 vertices. To prove this, we first note that to connect the 14 vertices we need a minimum of 13 edges, so the length of the shortest path must be at least $13 \times 1/\sqrt{2}$. A path of this length would move alternately between corners and face centres, but as there are 8 corners and 6 face centres this is impossible. At least one of the edges on the shortest path, therefore, must join two corners. So the length of the shortest path must be at least $1 + 12 \times 1/\sqrt{2}$. The diagrams show that such a path does exist so we are able to conclude that $1 + 6\sqrt{2}$ is indeed the length of the shortest path.

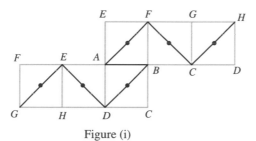   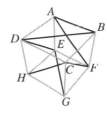

Figure (i)   Figure (ii)

25. B   Each exterior angle of a regular hexagon $= 360°$ $\div 6 = 60°$, so when sides HB and IC are produced to meet at A, an equilateral triangle, ABC, is created. Let the sides of this triangle be of length x. As BC, DE and FG are all parallel, triangles ABC, ADE and AFG are all equilateral. So $DE = DA = p + x$; $FG = FA = q + p + x$.

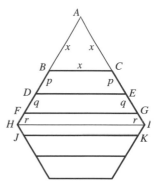

The perimeter of trapezium $BCED$
$= x + p + x + 2p = 2x + 3p$;

the perimeter of trapezium $DEGF$
$= (p + x) + (q + p + x) + 2q = 2x + 2p + 3q$;

the perimeter of hexagon $FGIKJH$
$= 2((q + p + x) + 2r) = 2x + 2p + 2q + 4r$.

So $2x + 3p = 2x + 2p + 3q$; hence $p = 3q$.
Also $2x + 2p + 3q = 2x + 2p + 2q + 4r$; hence $q = 4r$.
So $p : q : r = 12r : 4r : r = 12 : 4 : 1$.

IMC solutions 2006

C B D E B * A D C D B * C D E D A * B E E B D * A B B C D

1. **C**   Note that $\frac{1}{4} = \frac{6}{24}$ and $\frac{1}{6} = \frac{4}{24}$. So $\frac{5}{24}$ is half-way between them.

2. **B**   The configuration includes three pairs of small rings. The rings in each pair are separate from the rings in the other two pairs so at least three rings will need to be cut. If the ring in each pair which is connected to the large ring is cut, then all of the rings can be separated. So the minimum number of rings which need to be cut is three.

3. **D**   The values of the given options are 3, 7, 31, 63 and 127 respectively. All are prime, except 63. (*Note that $2^c - 1$ is never prime if c is composite. However, if p is prime, $2^p - 1$ is not necessarily prime. The smallest example of this occurs for p = 11: $2^{11} - 1 = 23 \times 89$.*)

4. **E**   Whatever number is placed in the fifth box, the median and mode of the numbers will both be 7. For the mean to equal 7, the total of the 5 numbers must be 35. This means that the missing number is 9.

5. **B**   Each pyramid has five faces, but the square base of each one is glued to the cube and therefore does not form a face of the star. So each pyramid contributes four faces to the star. As there are six such pyramids, the star has 24 faces.
   (It can be shown that the height of each of the pyramids is $1/\sqrt{2}$. If, and only if, the pyramids had been of height 1/2, however, then the angle between a triangular face of the pyramid and its square base would have been 45°. This would result in the solid having 12 faces rather than 24, as pairs of triangular faces would combine to form rhombi. The solid so formed is known as as a rhombic decahedron: a space-filling polyhedron.)
   (Diagram from http://dogfeathers.com/mark/rhdodec.html).

6. **A**   Turbo will take 3 hours to complete the 12 miles, whilst Harriet will take 1 hour 30 minutes. So Harriet should set off 1 hour 30 minutes after Turbo, that is at 9:45 am.

7. **D**   Statements A, B, and E may be made by the Queen of Spades, whether it is a day on which she is telling the truth or a day on which she is lying. She may also make statement C providing she is telling the truth that day. However, if she is telling the truth on a particular day then she could not make statement D since that would be a lie. Also, if she is not telling the truth on that day then she could not make statement D either, since that would then be a true statement. So she cannot make statement D.

8. **C**   The clock time in Melbourne when Sydney arrived was 32 hours (one complete day and 8 hours) ahead of the clock time in London when he left. So he arrived at 7:30 pm on Wednesday.

9. D   Note that one cannot remove two touching coins; for if you did, any third coin originally making up a triangle with them would then be slideable. Note also that it is possible to remove the centre coin and each of the coins in a corner of the frame without enabling any of the remaining coins to slide. However, as each remaining coin touched at least one of the removed coins, it is not possible to remove any further coins. If, instead, a coin other than one of these four was removed first, then it would be one of the middle pair of an edge. Four coins would have touched this coin, so that would leave five possible coins to remove. Four of the five coins would lie along an edge of the frame, with two of these forming a triangle with the fifth. Clearly, only one of the three coins which form a triangle may now be removed, together with only one of the other two coins as they are touching. So we conclude that the maximum number of coins which may be removed is four.

10. B   The lunch bill and tip total £28, so Gill and her friend should pay £14 each. As Gill has paid £25.50, she should now receive £25.50 − £14, that is £11.50.

11. C   At 8 o'clock, the obtuse angle between the hands of the clock is 120°. In the following six minutes, the minute hand turns though an angle of 36° whilst the hour hand turns through an angle of 3° in the same direction (clockwise!). So the obtuse angle between the hands increases by 33°.

12. D   Three of the shadows are possible, the first, third and fourth. The diagrams below show four positions obtained by rotating a cube about XY, a line through the midpoints of a pair of opposite edges. Three of the shadows in the question correspond to three of these positions. Though the second shadow matches the angles and four of the lengths given by the second position, it does not match the other two lengths and so is not possible.

In fact, the second shadow corresponds to a cuboid which is half a cube, as shown alongside.

[As it is quite difficult to rule out the second diagram without using a cube or calculator, in IMC 2006, 5 marks also given for answer E.]

13. E   Note that $x\%$ of $y = y\%$ of $x = xy/100$. So 2006% of 50 = 50% of 2006 = 1003.

14. D   The diagram shows that the two pieces will fit together to form a right-angled triangle which has base 8 and height 6. The length of the hypotenuse = $\sqrt{6^2 + 8^2}$, that is 10, so the perimeter of the triangle is 24.

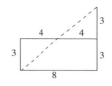

15. A   The mean of $1.\dot{2}$ and $2.\dot{1}$ is $\left(1.\dot{2} + 2.\dot{1}\right) \div 2 = 3.\dot{3} \div 2 = 1.\dot{6}.$

16. B Al and Bertie have £55 between them, so Chris and Di have £150 − £55, that is £95, between them. As Al and Chris have £65 between them, the difference between the amounts Al and Di have is £95 − £65.

17. E The profit made would be £14 999.50, which is 29 999 times the original price. So that gives a profit of 29 999 × 100%, that is 2 999 900%.

18. E Note that $4^x + 4^x + 4^x + 4^x = 4 \times 4^x = 4^{x+1}$. So $x + 1 = 16$.

19. B Each interior angle of a regular pentagon is 108°, whilst each interior angle of a regular hexagon is 120°. The non-regular pentagon in the centre of the diagram contains two angles which are interior angles of the regular hexagon, two angles which are interior angles of the regular pentagon and a fifth angle, the one marked $x°$. So
$x + 2 \times 120 + 2 \times 108 = 5 \times 108 = 540$. Hence $x = 84$.

20. D As n is clearly odd, the series may be written as
$1 + [-2 + 3] + [-4 + 5] + \ldots + [-(n-1) + n]$. So
$1 - 2 + 3 - 4 + 5 - 6 + \ldots + (n-2) - (n-1) + n = 1 + 1 + \ldots + 1 = \frac{1}{2}(n+1)$. So
$\frac{1}{2}(n + 1) = 2006$, that is $n = 4011$.

21. A Let T be the centre of the semicircle with diameter QR and let OT produced meet the circumference of the larger semicircle at U.

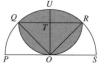

By symmetry, we note that OT is perpendicular to QR.

As $TR = TO = TQ$ (radii of semicircle), triangles ORT and OQT are both isosceles, right-angled triangles. So QOR is a right angle.

By Pythagoras' Theorem: $QR^2 = OQ^2 + OR^2 = 2^2 + 2^2 = 8$. So $QR = \sqrt{8} = 2\sqrt{2}$ and the radius of semicircle QOR is $\sqrt{2}$.

The area of the shaded region is equal to the area of semicircle QOR plus the area of the quadrant bounded by OQ, OR and arc QUR less the area of triangle OQR. So the required area is
$\frac{1}{2}\pi(\sqrt{2})^2 + \frac{1}{4}\pi 2^2 - \frac{1}{2} \times 2 \times 2 = \pi + \pi - 2 = 2\pi - 2$.

22. B First note that counters of the same colour form diagonal lines across the board. The diagrams show the board before and after the counters are added. In both cases, the board has been rotated 45° anticlockwise. Note that the red counters are shown as grey.

Now consider the board to consist of 15 horizontal rows of squares, numbered from 7 to −7 as shown. The only rows in which the colour of the squares on the board matches the colour of the counters are rows 7, 6, 1, 0, −5 and −6. These contain 1, 2, 7, 8, 3 and 2 squares respectively, so the required fraction is 23/64.

23. **B** Triangles QPR and RPS are similar since $\angle QPR = \angle RPS$ and $\angle RQP = \angle SRP$.

So $\frac{PR}{PS} = \frac{PQ}{PR}$. Hence $PR^2 = PQ \times PS = \frac{7}{3} \times \frac{48}{7} = 16$. So PR is 4 units long.

(*The geometric mean of x and y is defined to be $\sqrt{xy}$, so in this problem PR is the geometric mean of PQ and PS.*)

24. **C** Let r be the radius of the circle. Then, in the smaller square:

$$r^2 = \left(\sqrt{x}\right)^2 + \left(\tfrac{1}{2}\sqrt{x}\right)^2 = x + \tfrac{x}{4} = \tfrac{5x}{4}$$

and in the larger square:

$$r^2 = \left(\tfrac{1}{2}\sqrt{y}\right)^2 + \left(\tfrac{1}{2}\sqrt{y}\right)^2 = \tfrac{y}{4} + \tfrac{y}{4} = \tfrac{y}{2}$$

So $\tfrac{5x}{4} = \tfrac{y}{2}$ and we deduce that $x : y = 2 : 5$.

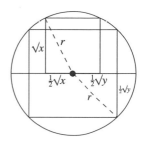

25. **D** First note that as j, l and m are all non-negative, the values of 5^j, 7^l and 11^m are all odd. However, the sum $5^j + 6^k + 7^l + 11^m$ is even, so we deduce that 6^k cannot be even and hence $k = 0$, that is $6^k = 1$. Now, for all positive integer values of j and m, the units digit of $5^j + 6^0 + 11^m$ is $5 + 1 + 1$, that is 7. So the units digit of 7^l is 9 and we deduce that $l = 2$ since 7, 49 and 343 are the only positive integer powers of 7 less than 2006. We now have $5^j + 6^0 + 7^2 + 11^m = 2006$, that is $5^j + 11^m = 1956$. The only positive integer powers of 11 less than 2006 are 11, 121 and 1331. These would require the value of 5^j to be 1945, 1835 and 625 respectively, and of these only 625 is a positive integer power of 5.

So $5^4 + 6^0 + 7^2 + 11^3 = 2006$.

SMC solutions 1997

*A C B E E * D B D D B * A D B D A * A B B E C * E C E A C*

1.   A $2 \times 4 + 2 = (2 \times 4) + 2 = 10$; the other options all give the answer 12.

2.   C   The five integers are "consecutive".

The third term is the middle term and so is equal to the average 10, while the second and fourth terms are equal to $10 - d$ and $10 + d$, where $d = 1$ is the common difference.

NOTE: (a) There is no need to work out the terms of the sequence.

(b) The same idea will work for any AP: the sum of two terms the same distance either side of the middle term is equal to twice the average.

3.   B   The area of a rhombus *ABCD* is equal to half the product of the diagonals *AC.BD*.

[A rhombus is a special parallelogram, so the diagonals *AC* and *BD* bisect each other – at *M* say.

The diagonal *AC* cuts the rhombus into two congruent isosceles triangles *ABC* and *CDA*.

The line joining the apex *B* of the isosceles triangle *ABC* to the mid-point *M* of the base *AC* is perpendicular to *AC*; ∴ △*ABC* has base *AC* and height *BD*/2, so has area *(AC/2).(BD/2)*. ∴ the rhombus *ABCD* has area *(AC.BD)/2*.]

4.   E   The smallest amount that cannot be paid with ≤ 4 coins is 38p.

[1p, 2p, 5p, 10p, 20p can all be paid with just one coin.

3p, 4p, 6p, 7p, 11p, 12p, 15p, 21p, 22p, 25p, 30p require two coins.

8p, 9p, 13p, 14p, 16p, 17p, 23p, 24p, 26p, 27p, 31p, 32p, 35p all require three coins.

18p (=10+5+2+1), 19p (=10+5+2+2), 28p (=20+5+2+1), 29p (=20+5+2+2), 33p (=20+10+2+1), 34p (=20+10+2+2), 36p (=20+10+5+1), 37p (=20+10+5+2), all require four coins. 38p cannot be paid with four coins.]

5.   E   The surface of the initial 2 by 2 by 2 arrangement consists of $6 \times 2^2 = 24$ unit squares. The surface of each unit cube consists of just 6 unit squares. Hence we have to leave at least 4 unit cubes to ensure a surface area of 24 unit squares.

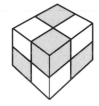

In fact, if one removes the unit cubes, with shaded faces, at the four corners, the resulting "shape" has a surface area of exactly 24 unit squares.

6.   D $240:120 = 2:1 = 110:55$; $300:180 = 5:3 = 350:210$. But $320:200 = 8:5$.

7. B   The entry for *Bernoulli* could be the first entry in Volume 2; it would then be right at the front – that is, on the *right* of Volume 2 as it stands on the shelf.

The entry for *Einstein* could be the last entry in Volume 3, so would be right at the back - on the *left* of Volume 3 as it stands on the shelf.

NOTE: There would be several entries under the name of "Bernoulli"!

In fact the Professor of Mathematics in the University of Basel was called Bernoulli for 105 years in a row. Three members of the family stand out: Jakob (1654-1705), Johann (1667-1748) and Daniel (1700-1782) all made major contributions to mathematics.

8. D   The first twelve students scored a total of $12 \times 6.5 = 78$ marks.

The remaining eight students might have scored any total between $8 \times 0 = 0$ and $8 \times 10 = 80$. Thus the twenty students could have a total score as low as $78 + 0 = 78$ marks, or as high as $78 + 80 = 158$ marks. Hence all we can say about the average M for the whole group is that it must be $\geqslant 78/20 = 3.9$ and $\leqslant 158/20 = 7.9$.

9. D   Let the cube have side length s. Using Pythagoras on the right angled triangle ABC (with $AB = BC = s$), we find $AC = s\sqrt{2}$.

Using Pythagoras on the right angled triangle ACG, we find $AG = s\sqrt{3}$.

Hence $\cos \angle CAG = AC/AG = \sqrt{(2/3)}$.

10. B $0.\dot{1} = 1/10$, so $0.\dot{n} = n/10$. $0.\dot{1} = 1/9$, so $0.\dot{n} = n/9$.

$\therefore (0.\dot{n})/(0.\dot{n}) = (n/10)/(n/9) = 9/10$.

11. A $999 = 9 \times 111 < 9 \times 9^3 = 9^4 < 99^9 < \left(9^3\right)^9 = 9^{27} < 9^{81} = \left(9^9\right)^9 < 9^{99} < 9^{\left(9^9\right)}$

12. D $1 + 2(1 + 2(1 + 2(1 + 2(1 + 2(1 + 2(1 + 2(1 + 2(1 + 2(1 + 2(1 + 2)))))))))))$
$$= 1 + 2 + 2^2 + 2^3 + 2^4 + 2^5 + 2^6 + 2^7 + 2^8 + 2^9 + 2^{10} + 2^{11}.$$
Now $\left(x^{n-1} + x^{n-2} + \ldots + x^2 + x + 1\right)(x - 1) = \left(x^n - 1\right)$

$\therefore 2^{11} + 2^{10} + 2^9 + \ldots + 2^2 + 2 + 1) = \left(2^{12} - 1\right)/(2 - 1) = 2^{12} - 1$.

13. B   Suppose Noel bought c cards at n pence each. Thus $n.c = 1560$. The extra (free) card effectively reduced the unit cost by 1p.

$$\therefore \quad (n + 1)(c - 1) = 1560$$
$$\therefore \quad nc + c - n - 1 = 1560$$
$$\therefore \quad c = n + 1 \text{ (since } nc = 1560)$$
$$\therefore \quad n.c = n(n + 1) = 1560$$
$$\therefore \quad 0 = n^2 + n - 1560 = (n - 39)(n + 40)$$
$$\therefore \quad n = 39 \text{ (since } n > 0).$$

Hence Noel could have bought 12 cards for £5 (with 32p change).

14. D   Suppose there are h pieces along each horizontal edge and v pieces along each vertical edge. Then $h.v = 1000 = 2^3.5^3$.

Thus the only possibilities for the pair $\{h, v\}$ are $\{1,1000\}$, $\{2, 500\}$, $\{4, 250\}$, $\{5, 200\}$, $\{8, 125\}$, $\{10, 100\}$, $\{20, 50\}$, $\{25, 40\}$.

The total number of edge pieces is $2h + 2v - 4 = 2(h + v - 2)$ (since $2h + 2v$ counts each of the four corners twice).

$\therefore$ $126 (= 2(25 + 40 - 2))$, $136 (= 2(20 + 50 - 2))$, $216 (= 2(10 + 100 - 2))$ are all possible; but 316 is not.

15. A   The exterior angle at D of triangle ADC is equal to the sum of the two interior opposite angles:

$$\therefore \angle BDC = \angle DAC + \angle DCA = \theta + (\angle ACB - \angle BCD)$$
$$= \theta + (\angle ACB - \theta) = \angle ACB = \angle DBC \text{ (given)}.$$

Hence $\triangle CBD$ is isosceles with the same angles as $\triangle ACB$.

$$\therefore AC/BC = BC/BD = BC/(AC/2)$$
$$\therefore AC^2 = 2.BC^2$$
$$\therefore BC^2 = AC^2 + AB^2 - 2.AC.AB. \cos\theta \text{ (by the cosine rule in } \triangle ABC)$$
$$\therefore BC^2 = (\sqrt{2}.BC)^2 + (\sqrt{2}.BC)^2 - 2.(\sqrt{2}.BC)(\sqrt{2}.BC) \cos\theta$$
$$\therefore \cos\theta = (3.BC^2)/(4.BC^2) = 3/4.$$

16. A   Each arc is $x/360$ times the full circumference.

$$\therefore \text{arc } AA' = (x/360)2\pi a, \text{ and arc } BB' = (x/360)2\pi b.$$

Now equate the lengths of the two routes (arc AA' direct and via arc BB').

$$\therefore (x/360)2\pi a = (a - b) + (x/360)2\pi b + (a - b)$$
$$\therefore (x/360)2\pi(a - b) = 2(a - b)$$
$$\therefore (x/360)\pi = 1$$
$$\therefore x = 360/\pi \approx 360/(22/7) = 1260/11 \approx 114.5.$$

17. B $f^2(x) = f(f(x)) = f\left(\frac{x-1}{x+1}\right) = \left(\frac{x-1}{x+1} - 1\right)/\left(\frac{x-1}{x+1} + 1\right) = -2/2x = -1/x$.

$\therefore f^4(x) = f^2(f^2(x)) = f^2(-1/x) = -1/[-1/x] = x.$

$\therefore f^6(x) = f^2(f^4(x)) = f^2(x) = -1/x.$

18. B   If (x, y) lies on the curve, so does $(x, -y)$: this excludes A, C.

Values of x which produce negative values of $\sin x$ do not feature: this excludes D. B is possible: this excludes E.

19. E   Vol(sand) = vol(cylinder) + vol(hemisphere) = $(\pi r^2).r + \frac{2}{3}\pi r^3 = \frac{5}{3}\pi r^3$.

When turned over, the conical end (volume $(\pi r^2/3)r$) fills up first, and the cylinder then fills to a height of $4r/3$ – a total height $r + 4r/3 = 7r/3$.

20. C The five options all have $h < h' < h''$. Label the triangle ABC so that h, h', h'' are the altitudes from A, B, C respectively. $\triangle ABC$ has area
$\Delta = ah/2 = bh'/2 = ch''/2$.

$$\therefore a > b > c \text{ (since } h < h' < h'').$$

Three positive lengths a, b, c with $a > b > c$ form the sides of a triangle precisely when $a < b + c$ (by the triangle inequality). This condition is equivalent to $a/2\Delta < b/2\Delta + c/2\Delta$; that is,

$$1/h < 1/h' + 1/h''.$$

The ratios A, B, D, E all satisfy this condition, but C does not.

21. E Suppose the large square has side s, and the small top left rectangle has vertical side of length x.

$\therefore AB = 1/x,\ CD = 3/x,\ EF = 2x$.

$\therefore TU = s - 4/x,\ TW = s - 3x$.

$\therefore s - 4/x = 2 - 3x$ (since $TUVW$ is a square – given)

$\therefore 3x = 4/x$, so $x = 2/\sqrt{3}$.

$\therefore$ perimeter of the bottom left rectangle
$= 2/x + 4x = 3/\sqrt{3} + 8/\sqrt{3} = 11/\sqrt{3}$.

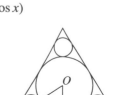

22. C $a^3 + b^3 = (a + b)(a^2 - ab + b^2)$

$$\therefore \sin^3 x + \cos^3 x = (\sin x + \cos x)(\sin^2 x - \sin x \cos x + \cos^2 x)$$

$$= (\sin x + \cos x)(1 - \sin x \cos x)$$

23. E $\triangle AOM$ is a 30-60-90 triangle, so $OA = 2OM$.
$\triangle AOM$ and $\triangle AO'M'$ are similar, and
$OO' = OM + O'M'$ (sum of two radii);

$$\therefore \frac{O'M'}{OM} = \frac{O'A}{OA} = \frac{OA - OO'}{OA} = 1 - \frac{OO'}{OA}$$

$$= 1 - \frac{(OM + O'M')}{2.OM} = \frac{1}{2} - \frac{OM'}{2.OM}$$

$$\therefore O'M' : OM = 1 : 3$$

$$\therefore \pi(O'M')^2 : \pi(OM)^2 = 1 : 9$$

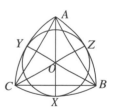

24. A Join AB, BC and CA.
Then $\triangle ABC$ is equilateral, with sides length 3cm.
The three medians meet at O, where
$$AO = BO = CO = (2/3) \times (3\sqrt{3}/2) = \sqrt{3}.$$
$$\therefore OX = OY = OZ = 3 - \sqrt{3}.$$
Hence the circle centre O through X, Y, Z has area
$$\pi(3 - \sqrt{3})^2 = \pi(12 - 6\sqrt{3}) = 6\pi(2 - \sqrt{3}).$$

25. C   Let A be the apex of the cone, O the centre of the sphere, and C the point where the sphere touches the base of the cone. Let P be any point where the sphere touches the side of the cone, and let B be the point where the line AP meets the base of the cone.

Let $OP = r = OC$ be the radius of the sphere.

$\triangle ABC$ and $\triangle AOP$ are similar.

$\therefore$ $BC/OP = AC/AP = (AO + OC)/AP$

$\therefore$ $BC/r = [r/\sin\alpha + r]/[r/\tan\alpha]$

$\therefore$ $BC = r(1 + \sin\alpha)/\cos\alpha$

$\therefore$ volume of sphere $= \mathcal{S} = 4\pi r^3/3$

volume of cone $= \mathcal{C} = (1/3)\pi[r(1 + \sin\alpha)/\cos\alpha]^2 \times [r/\sin\alpha + r]$

$\therefore$ $\mathcal{S}/\mathcal{C} = 4\left[\left(\dfrac{1 + \sin\alpha}{\cos\alpha}\right)^2\left(\dfrac{1 + \sin\alpha}{\sin\alpha}\right)\right]^{-1} = 4\sin\alpha\cos^2\alpha/(1 + \sin\alpha)^3$

$\qquad = \dfrac{4\sin\alpha\cos^2\alpha(1 - \sin\alpha)^3}{(1 - \sin^2\alpha)^3} = \dfrac{4\sin\alpha(1 - \sin\alpha)^3}{\cos^4\alpha}.$

SMC solutions 1998

A D C B C * E D D D C * B B D E B * D A D B A * C D E A E

1. **A**   The sum, 60, is 5 times the middle number. So the middle number is 12. The numbers are 8, 10, 12, 14, 16.

    Note: consecutive even numbers form an arithmetic sequence and the middle term of such a sequence with an odd number of terms is always the mean of all the terms.

2. **D**   Of the thirty pupils, 8 are left-handed. In the extreme case, these will all be girls. So the smallest number of girls who could be right-handed is 6.

3. **C**   Multiplying the decimal part of each option by 8 gives 0.40, 1.20, 2, 2.8 and 3.6.

4. **B**   The diameter of the smaller circle and the radius of the larger circle are equal. Letting the radius of the smaller circle be r, the areas are πr^2 and $\pi (2r)^2 = 4\pi r^2$ so the smaller circle is $\frac{1}{4}$ of the larger.

    Note: this is an example of the property that in an enlargement the area scale factor is the square of the linear factor.

5. **C**   The perimeter of the rectangle is 12 cm. So each side of the square is 3 cm.

6. **E**   The question really asks how many of the first 15 positive integers can be expressed as the sum of 4 or fewer perfect squares. These can be listed as follows:–

    $1 = 1^2$; $2 = 1^2 + 1^2$; $3 = 1^2 + 1^2 + 1^2$; $4 = 2^2$. Expressions for 5, 6, 7 and 8 can be obtained by adding 2^2 to each of the ones already given. $9 = 3^2$ and expressions for 10, 11, 12, 13, 14, and 15 can be obtained by adding 3^2 to the ones for 1, 2, 3, 4, 5 and 6.

    Note: In fact, the French mathematician Lagrange proved in 1770 that every positive integer can be expressed as the sum of four squares.

7. **D**   Let Mary's height at age 5 be h. So at age 10 her height is $1.3h$ and by age 15 this will be $1.2 \times 1.3h = 1.56h$.

8. **D**   Squaring each number gives 240, 250, 245, 243 and 242. In terms of size, the middle of these is 243.

9. **D**   Using their initial to denote a candidate's mark gives:–

    $P + N = 32; P + F = 26; N + F = 36$. Adding these three equations gives $2P + 2N + 2F = 94$, hence $P + N + F = 47$. Thus $47 + G = 4 \times 16$ giving $G = 17$.

    Biographical note: although the lives of Pascal and Fermat overlapped with the lives of the other two mathematicians, Galileo died in 1642, the year in which Newton was born (on Christmas Day).

10. **C**   There are 60×60 seconds in an hour. In a day there are $24 \times 60 \times 60 = 24 \times 4 \times 15 \times 60 = 96 \times 900$ which is roughly $10^2 \times 10^3 = 10^5$.

11. B $\dfrac{1647}{8235} = \dfrac{1}{5}$ becomes $\dfrac{167}{835} = \dfrac{1}{5}$ which in turn becomes $\dfrac{17}{85} = \dfrac{1}{5}$. Hence
$D = 85$ and $C = 17$ so $D - C = 68$.

12. B $\triangle APB$ is equilateral hence $\angle ABP = 60°$.
But $BC = AB = PB$ so $\triangle PBC$ is isosceles with
$\angle PBC = 135° - 60° = 75°$.
$\therefore \angle BPC = \frac{1}{2}(180 - 75)°$ and
$\angle APC = 52.5° + 60°$.

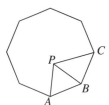

13. D
$$x = \left(\dfrac{1}{4}\right)^{\frac{1}{2}} = \sqrt{\dfrac{1}{4}} = \dfrac{1}{2}$$
$$\therefore x^{-x} = \left(\dfrac{1}{2}\right)^{-\frac{1}{2}} = \left(2^{-1}\right)^{-\frac{1}{2}} = 2^{\frac{1}{2}} = \sqrt{2}.$$

14. E AB is a diameter so $\angle ACB = 90°$.
$$\therefore CB^2 = AB^2 - AC^2$$
$$= 400 - 144 = 256$$
$$CB = 16$$

15. B

$2d$	d
$V\,\mathrm{ms}^{-1}$	$U\,\mathrm{ms}^{-1}$
t_1	t_2

$$t_1 = \dfrac{2d}{V}; t_2 = \dfrac{d}{U}$$
$$\therefore \dfrac{2d}{V} + \dfrac{d}{U} = T$$
$$d\left(\dfrac{2}{V} + \dfrac{1}{U}\right) = T$$
$$d(2U + V) = TUV$$
$$\therefore 3d = 3TUV / (2U + V)$$

16. D Number of years $= \dfrac{49}{6} \times \dfrac{48}{5} \times \dfrac{47}{4} \times \dfrac{46}{3} \times \dfrac{45}{2} \times \dfrac{44}{1} \div 52$
$$= 49 \times 1 \times 47 \times 46 \times 3 \times 44 \div 52$$
$$\approx 50^3 \times 3 = 375\,000.$$
*Note: 375000 is clearly an overestimate since $49 \times 1 \times 47 \times 46$ is less than 50^3
and $3 \times 44 \div 52$ is less than 3.*

17. A Re-ordering $(x - 1)(x^4 + 1)(x^2 + 1)(x + 1) = (x - 1)(x + 1)(x^2 + 1)(x^4 + 1)$
$$= (x^2 - 1)(x^2 + 1)(x^4 + 1) = (x^4 - 1)(x^4 + 1) = x^8 - 1$$
*Note: $(x - 1)(x^4 + 1)(x^2 + 1)(x + 1)$ has value 0 when $x = 1$. This enables B, C
and D to be eliminated.*

18. D Curved surface area of small cylinder $= 2\pi r \times 4r = 8\pi r^2$.
Curved surface area of large cylinder $= 4\pi r \times 4r = 16\pi r^2$.
Area of each end $= \pi (2r)^2 - \pi r^2 = 3\pi r^2$.
Total surface area $= 8\pi r^2 + 16\pi r^2 + 2 \times 3\pi r^2 = 30\pi r^2$.

19. B $\cos \theta = \frac{1}{2}; \sin^2 \theta = \frac{3}{4}; \sin \theta = \pm \frac{1}{2}\sqrt{3}$

$\sin 2\theta = 2 \cos \theta \sin \theta = 2 \times \frac{1}{2} \times (\pm \frac{1}{2}\sqrt{3}) = \pm \frac{1}{2}\sqrt{3}$

Note: $\sin 2\theta$ is equal to $2 \cos \theta \sin \theta$ for all values of θ and since in this case $\cos \theta = \frac{1}{2}$, $\sin 2\theta$ will also equal $\sin \theta$.

20. A   Space diagonal of the cube is 1 metre.
So, using x as the side of the cube

$$3x^2 = 1$$

$$x^2 = \frac{1}{3} = \text{area of one face}$$

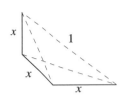

$\therefore$ total area of all six faces is 2 m^2.

21. C $3 \oplus 5 \rightarrow 4$ $3 \oplus 6 \rightarrow 4$ $4 \oplus 6 \rightarrow 4$ $4 \oplus 8 \rightarrow 4$

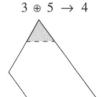

Note: the best way to see if $x \oplus y \rightarrow 4$ is possible is probably to start with a quadrilateral and test to see if you can form a polygon with y sides by removing a polygon with x sides.

22. D   Points inside the triangle ABC which are closer to AB are to the left of AP. So the probability is the ratio of the area of $\triangle ABP$ to the area of $\triangle ABC$ which is the ratio of BP to BC since the triangles have the same height. BP to BC is equal to $\tan 30° : \tan 60°$ i.e. $1/\sqrt{3} : \sqrt{3} = 1 : 3$.

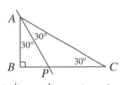

[Alternatively, draw the perpendicular from P to AC to show three congruent triangles.]

23. E   The small circle can be enlarged to the size of the other circle by using a scale factor of R/r. So if A and B are the centres of the circles

$$\frac{R}{r} = \frac{OB}{OA} = \frac{r\sqrt{2} + r + R}{r\sqrt{2}}$$

$$\sqrt{2}R = r\sqrt{2} + r + R$$

$$\frac{R}{r} = \frac{\sqrt{2} + 1}{\sqrt{2} - 1} = \frac{(\sqrt{2} + 1)^2}{(\sqrt{2} - 1)(\sqrt{2} + 1)} = 3 + 2\sqrt{2}.$$

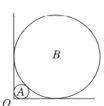

24. A   This *could* be done by using the quadratic formula and manipulating surds. However, a neater way is

$$x^2 - 3x + 1 = 0 \Rightarrow x - 3 + 1/x = 0 \Rightarrow x + 1/x = 3.$$

Now, squaring both sides, $9 = (x + 1/x)^2 = x^2 + 2 + 1/x^2$. Hence $x^2 + 1/x^2 = 7$.

25. E $PQ^2 = (\sqrt{2})^2 + (\sqrt{2})^2 = 4 \Rightarrow PQ = 2 \Rightarrow$ $OP = 1$. Hence triangles APO and BPO are isosceles with $\angle APQ = \angle BPQ = 135°$. The area of each of these triangles is $\frac{1}{2} \times 1 \times 1 \times \sin 135° = 1/(2\sqrt{2})$. Also $\angle AOB = \angle AOP + \angle BOP = 45°$. The shaded area

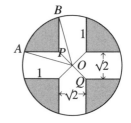

$$APB = \text{sector } AOB - 2 \times \frac{1}{2\sqrt{2}}$$

$$= \frac{1}{8}\pi \, OA^2 - \frac{1}{\sqrt{2}}$$

$$= \frac{1}{8}\pi \left(1^2 + 1^2 - 2\cos 135°\right) - \frac{1}{\sqrt{2}}$$

$$= \frac{1}{8}\pi \left(2 + \sqrt{2}\right) - 1/\sqrt{2}.$$

Multiplying by 4 gives $\pi\left(1 + \dfrac{1}{\sqrt{2}}\right) - 2\sqrt{2} = \dfrac{\pi\left(2 + \sqrt{2}\right)}{2} - 2\sqrt{2}.$

Note: as an alternative to using the cosine rule to calculate OA, it is possible to apply Pythagoras' Theorem giving

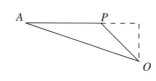

$$OA^2 = \left(1 + \frac{1}{\sqrt{2}}\right)^2 + \left(\frac{1}{\sqrt{2}}\right)^2 = 2 + \sqrt{2}.$$

SMC solutions 1999

*C D D C B * B D B C D * E E C A E * D C A C E * A E B A B*

1. **C** The prime numbers less than 20 are 2, 3, 5, 7, 11, 13, 17, and 19.

2. **D** If January 1st (or, in a leap year, January 1st or January 2nd) falls on a Sunday, then there will be 53 Sundays in that particular year.

3. **D** The two shaded triangles will overlap when the 'net' is folded.

4. **C** The reductions would be A 20%; C $33\frac{1}{3}$ %; D 30%; E 25%. B might be a "special offer", but is not one which should be accepted!

5. **B** 17 hours and 21 minutes = 1041 minutes and the average speed is therefore slightly less than 40 decimal places per minute.

6. **B** The percentage increase = $\dfrac{500 - 40}{40} \times 100\% = \dfrac{460}{40} \times 100\% = 1150\%$.

7. **D** Let the exterior angle be $x°$. Then $x + 4x = 180$ and therefore $x = 36$.
As is the case in all convex polygons, the sum of the exterior angles = 360° and therefore the number of sides = 360/36 = 10.

8. **B** $x - y = 9$; $x + y = 99$. Adding gives $2x = 108$ and therefore $x = 54$ and hence $y = 45$.
The ratio $x:y = 54:45 = 6:5$.
(As we are interested only in the ratio rather than the numbers themselves, the problem could be reduced to finding the ratio of two numbers which differ by 1 and have sum 11.)

9. **C** All of the positive integers from 1 to 50 inclusive must be factors of 50!.
$51 = 3 \times 17$ and $52 = 2 \times 26$ which means that these two numbers are also factors of 50!. 53 is prime and is not a factor of 50!.

10. **D** The values are, approximately, A 45; B $1 \times 30 = 30$; C $20 \times 10 = 200$; D 200 $\times 3 = 600$; E $2000 \times 0 = 0$.

11. **E** In the first row, any one of 5 letters could be circled. In the second row, any one of 4 letters could be circled since one column has now been occupied. Similarly, in the third row, any one of three letters could be circled and so on.
The number of different ways is therefore $5 \times 4 \times 3 \times 2 \times 1 = 120$.
(Notice that this is 5! as in solution to 9.)

12. **E** The White Rabbit must have been speaking on January 1st of this year. Two days earlier, December 30th, Alice was still thirteen and her fourteenth birthday was the following day, December 31st. She will, therefore, be fifteen on December 31st of this year and her sixteenth birthday will be on December 31st next year.

13. C   As we are given, $AO = \frac{1}{3}AC$; therefore
$AA' = \frac{2}{3}AC$ since $OA' = OA$.

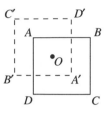

Thus the area of overlap is the area of a square
whose side is $\frac{2}{3}$ of the length of the side of square
$ABCD$ i.e. the area of a square of side 2 cm.

14. A   The line $y = 3x + 4$ intersects the axes at $\left(-\frac{4}{3}, 0\right)$ and $(0, 4)$. Its reflection
in the line $y = -x$ will therefore intersect the axes at $(-4, 0)$ and $\left(0, \frac{4}{3}\right)$. The
line through these points has gradient $\frac{1}{3}$ and therefore its equation is
$y = \frac{1}{3}x + \frac{4}{3}$ or $3y = x + 4$.
*(In general, the image of the point (a, b) after reflection in the line $y = -x$ is the
point $(-b, -a)$.)*

15. E $120 = 2^3 \times 3 \times 5$; $144 = 2^4 \times 3^2$; $240 = 2^4 \times 3 \times 5$;
$3000 = 2^3 \times 3 \times 5^3$; $12100 = 2^2 \times 5^2 \times 11^2$. The product of the three
numbers must have 6 prime factors, not necessarily all different, but with no
prime factor repeated more than 3 times. Of these, only 12100 satisfies this
condition. The three numbers are 10 (2×5), 22 (2×11) and 55 (5×11).

16. D x must be closer to 1000 than it is to 999 and also closer to 1000 than it is to 1010.

17. C   Let Jon's and Jan's ages be $3x$ and x respectively. Then $3x - 3 = 4(x - 3)$
which gives $x = 9$. Therefore Jon is 27 and Jan is 9. If the ratio will be 2 : 1
in y years time then $27 + y = 2(9 + y)$ which gives $y = 9$. In 9 years time,
Jon will be 36 and Jan will be 18.

18. A   Let the radii of the outer and inner circles be R and r
respectively. Then, by the Theorem of Pythagoras:
$R^2 = r^2 + p^2$ and therefore $R^2 - r^2 = p^2$. The area of the
shaded region $= \pi R^2 - \pi r^2 = \pi(R^2 - r^2) = \pi p^2$.

19. C   By the Theorem of Pythagoras, $QR = \sqrt{8}$ cm $= 2\sqrt{2}$ cm,
$QS = \sqrt{5}$ cm and $RS = \sqrt{5}$ cm. If T is the midpoint of
QR, then $TS^2 = \left(\sqrt{5}\right)^2 - \left(\sqrt{2}\right)^2 = 5 - 2 = 3$ and
therefore $TS = \sqrt{3}$ cm. The area of triangle
$QRS = \frac{1}{2}QR \times TS = \left(\sqrt{2} \times \sqrt{3}\right)$ cm$^2 = \sqrt{6}$ cm^2.

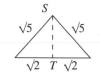

20. E $1 + 2 + 3 + 4 + 5 + \ldots + n = \frac{1}{2}n(n + 1)$.
Therefore the terms in the sequence with positions $\frac{1}{2}(n - 1)n + 1$ to
$\frac{1}{2}n(n + 1)$ inclusive will all be n. Now $\frac{1}{2} \times 62 \times 63 = 1953$ and
$\frac{1}{2} \times 63 \times 64 = 2016$. Therefore from the 1954th term to the 2016th term
inclusive will all be 63.

21. A   B cannot be prime since 111 is clearly a factor of it; C cannot be prime since
it equals 2999×1001 (difference of two squares); the units digit of D will be
5 and therefore 5 must be a factor of it whilst the units digit of E is 0 and
therefore it cannot be prime either since both 2 and 5 will be factors of it.

22. E

 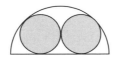

Let the radius of each large semicircle be R. Then $\pi R^2 = 4$. The circle in the left-hand diagram has radius $R/2$ and therefore its area is $\pi(R/2)^2 = (\pi R^2)/4 = 1$. Let the radii of the circles in the right-hand diagram be r. Then $R = \sqrt{2}\,r + r$.

Therefore $r = \dfrac{R}{\sqrt{2} + 1} = \dfrac{R(\sqrt{2} - 1)}{(\sqrt{2} + 1)(\sqrt{2} - 1)} = R(\sqrt{2} - 1)$.

The grey shaded area =

$$2\pi r^2 = 2\pi R^2(\sqrt{2} - 1)^2 = 2 \times 4 \times (2 - 2\sqrt{2} + 1) = 24 - 16\sqrt{2}.$$

The difference in areas is therefore $23 - 16\sqrt{2}$.

23. B

$$\frac{2n + y}{n - 2} = \frac{2n - 4}{n - 2} + \frac{y + 4}{n - 2} = 2 + \frac{y + 4}{n - 2} \qquad (n \neq 2).$$

Thus $(2n + y)/(n - 2)$ is an integer if and only if $(y + 4)/(n - 2)$ is an integer. As n varies, the integer values taken by $(y + 4)/(n - 2)$ are all the integers which divide exactly into $y + 4$. There are exactly 4 of these if and only if $y + 4$ is prime. They are $\{(y+4), -(y+4), 1, -1\}$. Thus the integer values of the expression will be $2 + y + 4 = y + 6$; $2 - (y + 4) = -(y + 2)$; 3 and 1. For $1 \leqslant y \leqslant 20$, the values of y for which $y + 4$ is prime are 1, 3, 7, 9, 13, 15 and 19.

24. A If the original tile is an isosceles trapezium made from three equilateral triangles then a quadrilateral (which is also an isosceles trapezium) will result.

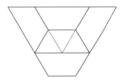

25. B

$$S = \frac{1}{2} + \frac{1}{4} + \frac{2}{8} + \frac{3}{16} + \frac{5}{32} + \frac{8}{64} + \frac{13}{128} + \frac{21}{256} + \frac{34}{512} + \ldots$$

$$= \frac{1}{2} + \frac{1}{4} + \left(\frac{1}{8} + \frac{1}{8}\right) + \left(\frac{1}{16} + \frac{2}{16}\right) + \left(\frac{2}{32} + \frac{3}{32}\right) + \left(\frac{3}{64} + \frac{5}{64}\right) + \left(\frac{5}{128} + \frac{8}{128}\right) + \ldots$$

$$= \frac{1}{2} + \left(\frac{1}{8} + \frac{1}{16} + \frac{2}{32} + \frac{3}{64} + \frac{5}{128} + \ldots\right) + \left(\frac{1}{4} + \frac{1}{8} + \frac{2}{16} + \frac{3}{32} + \frac{5}{64} + \frac{8}{128} + \ldots\right)$$

$$= \frac{1}{2} + \frac{1}{4}\left(\frac{1}{2} + \frac{1}{4} + \frac{2}{8} + \frac{3}{16} + \frac{5}{32} + \ldots\right) + \frac{1}{2}\left(\frac{1}{2} + \frac{1}{4} + \frac{2}{8} + \frac{3}{16} + \frac{5}{32} + \frac{8}{64} + \ldots\right)$$

$$= \frac{1}{2} + \frac{1}{4}S + \frac{1}{2}S = \frac{1}{2} + \frac{3}{4}S$$

Therefore $\quad \dfrac{1}{4}S = \dfrac{1}{2} \quad$ and so $\quad S = 2$.

SMC solutions 2000

D D C E A * D D B B C * A B B E A * C D E A E * A B C E C

1. D The units digit of the product is 3; therefore the remainder when that number is divided by 5 is also 3.

2. D $\frac{1}{81} = 0{\cdot}012345 + 0{\cdot}00000067\ldots$; therefore $\frac{2}{81} = 0{\cdot}024690 + 0{\cdot}0000013\ldots$ $= 0{\cdot}0246913\ldots = 0{\cdot}024691$ to six decimal places.

3. C Annakin has 5 coins and Obi-Wan Kenobi has 7.

4. E The average time each man took per seat is approximately $(27 \times 60 \times 60 \div 32000)$ seconds $= (27 \times 9 \div 80)$ seconds ≈ 3 seconds.

5. A Let AB and AD be of length b and h respectively. Then the area of $ABCD = bh$ and the area of $ABQP = \frac{1}{2}b\left(\frac{h}{2} + \frac{h}{3}\right) = \frac{5bh}{12}$. Thus the required ratio $= \frac{5}{12}$.

6. D The percentage increase $= \frac{58.1}{15.2} \times 100 \approx 400\,\%$.

7. D The shaded area in Y is clearly half the area of the hexagon and the diagram on the right demonstrates why the shaded areas in X and Z are also both equal to half the area of the hexagon.

8. B Let the distance between Newcastle and South Shields be x miles. Then the time for the whole journey is $\left(\frac{x}{30} + \frac{x}{40}\right)$ hours $= \frac{7x}{120}$ hours. Thus the average speed is $\left(2x \div \frac{7x}{120}\right)$ mph $= \frac{240}{7}$ mph $= 34\frac{2}{7}$ mph.

9. B $a^2 - b^2 = (a + b)(a - b)$. Thus $\frac{(61^2 - 39^2)}{(51^2 - 49^2)} = \frac{100 \times 22}{100 \times 2} = 11$.

10. C The dotted line shows the locus of P as the white square slides around the black square. The locus is a square of side 16 cm and hence P moves through a distance of 64 cm.
(Note: It may be shown that the the total distance moved by P is 64 cm, irrespective of the position of P on the white square.)

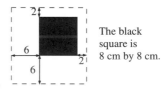

The black square is 8 cm by 8 cm.

11. A B cannot be true since $a + b > a$ but $a \div b \leqslant a$; C cannot be true since $a - b < a$ but $a \times b \geqslant a$; similarly, D cannot be true. Furthermore, E cannot be true since $(\sqrt{a} + \sqrt{b})^2 \neq a + b$. However, A is true if $a = 4$ and $b = 2$.

12. B   If the number of the year is even then it is either a power of 2, namely $2^5 \times 4^3$ or $2^3 \times 4^5$, both of which are greater than 2025, or it is $2^a \times 3^b$ or $2^a \times 5^b$, but no number between 2001 and 2024 is of this form. If the number is odd then it is either $3^4 \times 5^2$, which is 2025, or $3^2 \times 5^4$, which is much greater. Therefore 2025 is the next number of the given form.

13. B   New area $= \dfrac{1}{2}\left(\dfrac{9a}{10} + \dfrac{9b}{10}\right) \times \dfrac{11h}{10} = \dfrac{99}{100} \times \dfrac{1}{2}(a+b)h = 99\%$ of previous area of trapezium.

14. E   Cross-sections parallel to the end faces and the base give a triangle and rectangle respectively. A cross-section through points A, B, C and D gives a trapezium, while a cross-section through points A, E, F, C and D gives a pentagon. In order to obtain a hexagon, the cross-section would need to cut six edges of the prism and this is impossible.

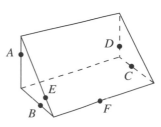

15. A   Let the 3 three-digit numbers be $100a + 10b + c$; $100d + 10e + f$; $100g + 10h + i$ where $a, b, c, d, e, f, g, h, i$ represent the digits 1 to 9 in some order.
Then $a + b + c + d + e + f + g + h + i = 45$.
The sum of the three numbers is
$100(a + d + g) + 10(b + e + h) + (c + f + i)$
$= 99(a+d+g) + 9(b+e+h) + (a+d+g) + (b+e+h) + (c+f+i)$
$= 99(a+d+g) + 9(b+e+h) + 45 = 9\big(11(a+d+g) + (b+e+h) + 5\big)$.
The sum must, therefore, be a multiple of 9 and 1500 is the only one of the options which is not a multiple of 9.
(Note: a complete solution should check that the other four options are possible:
$1503 = 216 + 538 + 749$; $1512 = 125 + 638 + 749$; $1521 = 124 + 638 + 759$;
$1539 = 132 + 648 + 759$.)

16. C   The cross-section of the 20 m tape has area $\pi\left(4^2 - 3^2\right)$ cm^2 $= 7\pi$ cm^2. Therefore, the 80 m tape should have a cross-section of area 28π cm^2. Hence, the outer radius of the 80 m roll will be approximately $\sqrt{37}$ cm.

17. D $(a+b+c)^3 = a^3 + b^3 + c^3 + 3a^2b + 3ab^2 + 3b^2c + 3bc^2 + 3c^2a + 3ca^2 + 6abc$

$= a^3 + b^3 + c^3 + 3(a+b+c)(ab+bc+ca) - 9abc + 6abc$

Hence: $a^3 + b^3 + c^3 = (a+b+c)^3 - 3(a+b+c)(ab+bc+ca) + 3abc$.

18. E $x^2 - 6x + 11 = (x-3)^2 + 2$. When the curve is rotated $180°$ about the origin, the equation of the new curve will be $y = -(x+3)^2 - 2$ i.e. $y = -x^2 - 6x - 9 - 2$ i.e. $y = -x^2 - 6x - 11$.
(Note: the image of point (a, b) under a $180°$ rotation about the origin is the point $(-a, -b)$. An alternative method, therefore, is to replace x and y in the original equation by $-x$ and $-y$ respectively.)

19. A $\angle ACB = \frac{1}{2}\alpha$ (angle subtended by an arc at the centre of a circle is twice the angle subtended at the circumference) and, similarly, $\angle CAD = \frac{1}{2}\beta$. Therefore $\angle AXB = \frac{1}{2}\alpha - \frac{1}{2}\beta$ (the exterior angle of a triangle is equal to the sum of the two interior opposite angles).

20. E   Any list whose product is a maximum does not contain any 1s since one 1 and one n could be replaced by one $n + 1$ and this would contribute $n + 1$ to the product rather than n. We can also say that any list of maximum product would contain a maximum of two 2s, since any three 2s could be replaced by two 3s which would contribute 9 to the product rather than 8. Furthermore, it would contain a maximum of one 4 since two 4s could be replaced by one 2 and two 3s thereby contributing 18 to the product rather than 16. It would not contain any number greater than 4 since $2(n - 2) > n$ when $n > 4$ and therefore the product would be increased by replacing one n with one 2 and one $n - 2$. Any list of numbers whose product is a maximum, therefore, consists of two 2s and thirty-two 3s or one 4 and thirty-two 3s and the maximum product is $2^2 \times 3^{32}$.

21. A   Tangents to a circle from an exterior point are equal in length.
Thus $AD = AB = 1$ and $CD = \sqrt{2} - 1$.
In $\triangle OCD$, $\angle ODC = 90°$ and $\angle OCD = 45°$.
Therefore $\triangle OCD$ is isosceles and hence radius $OD = CD = \sqrt{2} - 1$.

22. B $\left(\dfrac{a + b}{a - b}\right)^2 = \dfrac{a^2 + 2ab + b^2}{a^2 - 2ab + b^2} = \dfrac{6ab + 2ab}{6ab - 2ab} = 2$. As $0 < b < a$, $\dfrac{a + b}{a - b} > 0$ and hence $\left(\dfrac{a + b}{a - b}\right) = \sqrt{2}$.

23. C   In the tournament, there are $\frac{1}{2} \times 2n \times (2n - 1)$ matches between two right-handed players; $\frac{1}{2} \times n \times (n - 1)$ matches between two left-handed players and $2n \times n$ matches between a right-handed player and a left-handed player.
Let the number of matches in which right-handed players beat left-handed players be x. Then:
number of matches won by right-handed players is $\frac{1}{2} \times 2n \times (2n - 1) + x$.
number of matches won by left-handed players is $\frac{1}{2} \times n \times (n - 1) + 2n \times n - x$.
Thus: $3\big(n(2n - 1) + x\big) = 4\big(\frac{1}{2}n(n - 1) + 2n^2 - x\big)$ that is,
$7x = 4n^2 + n = n(4n + 1)$.
Since there are fewer than 20 players, $n \leqslant 6$ and the only possible value of n for which $4n^2 + n$ is a multiple of 7 is 5. Hence $n = 5$ and $x = 15$. There are 10 right-handed players and 5 left-handed players. The number of matches won by right-handers is $45 + 15 = 60$ and the number of matches won by left-handers is $10 + 35 = 45$.

24. E Squaring both sides of the equation gives $y = x - 2\sqrt{17x} + 17$. The right-hand side will be a positive integer if x is of the form $17n^2$ for an integer $n \geqslant 2$, and the equation then becomes
$y = 17n^2 - 34n + 17 = 17(n - 1)^2$.

As there are infinitely many $n \geqslant 2$, there are infinitely many pairs of positive integers (x, y) which satisfy the equation e.g. $(68, 17)$, $(153, 68)$, $(272, 153)$ etc.

25. C The diagram shows points A, B and C, the centres of circles C_1, C_2 and C_3 respectively.

Let the radius of circle C_3 be r.

The positions of points D, E and F are as shown on the diagram.

In $\triangle ACE$:

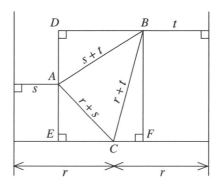

$$AE^2 = AC^2 - EC^2$$

$$= (r + s)^2 - (r - s)^2 = 4rs.$$

In $\triangle BCF$:

$$BF^2 = BC^2 - CF^2 = (r + t)^2 - (r - t)^2 = 4rt.$$

Hence $DA = DE - AE = BF - AE = 2\sqrt{rt} - 2\sqrt{rs}$.

Also, $DB = 2r - (s + t)$.

Therefore, in $\triangle ABD$:

$$(s + t)^2 = (2r - (s + t))^2 + (2\sqrt{rt} - 2\sqrt{rs})^2$$

i.e. $(s + t)^2 = 4r^2 - 4r(s + t) + (s + t)^2 + 4rt - 8\sqrt{rt}\sqrt{rs} + 4rs$

i.e. $0 = 4r^2 - 8r\sqrt{st}$

i.e. $r = 0$ (impossible) or $r = 2\sqrt{st}$.

SMC solutions 2001

C D D A D * C E B B E * A B D A A * B C E C C * C E A E D

1. **C** 100 hours equal four days and four hours so the candle will burn out at 4pm on Thursday.

2. **D** Since 10^7 is not divisible by 11, then neither is $10^7 - 11$ nor $10^7 + 11$. Therefore, the correct answer is either B or D.
$10^7 - 1 = 9\,999\,999 = 11 \times 909090 + 9$. Therefore
$10^7 + 1 = 11 \times 909090 + 11$. Hence D is the correct answer.

3. **D** There are six quadrilaterals shaped ⬭ and six shaped ◺.

4. **A** To have lost the fewest games, there need to be as many draws as possible. However, since 21 is odd, there needs to be at least one win. That is possible with 8 draws, leaving 11 games lost.

5. **D** Since the numbers offered are all odd, they need to be the sum of an even prime and an odd prime. But 2 is the only even prime so we need a number which is not two more than a prime. Since $13 = 2 + 11$; $33 = 2 + 31$; $43 = 2 + 41$ and $73 = 2 + 71$, we have $53 = 2 + 3 \times 17$ as the answer.

6. **C** Since the four numbers are symmetrical about the mean of the group, they must have the same mean, 21, giving their total as 84.
Alternatively, it is possible to state that the original numbers must be 15, 17, 19, 21, 23, 25, 27 (since the numbers are given as consecutive and odd). Hence the required sum is $15 + 19 + 23 + 27 = 84$.

7. **E** For each row that the apprentice plants, the gardener has planted one more in his previous row. The apprentice plants 50 rows and in addition the gardener plants the last one.

8. **B** Joining A to C and each of A, C and E to the centre of the hexagon divides it into six congruent triangles four of which make up $ABCE$. So the area of $ABCE$ is $\frac{2}{3}$ of 60.

9. **B** Since 6 and 9 are not prime, C and D cannot provide counter-examples. For 3, both parts are true (since 11 is prime) but since $5^2 + 2 = 27$ is not prime, B does provide a counter-example.

10. **E** There are six boxes adjacent to the box labelled **X**. However, each of the numbers 2, 3, 4, 5, 6 and 7 has only five numbers which are not adjacent to it and therefore the labelled box must contain 1 or 8.

11. **A** Since $x = \frac{1}{y}$, it follows that $y = \frac{1}{x}$. Hence
$\left(x + \frac{1}{x}\right)\left(y - \frac{1}{y}\right) = (x + y)(y - x) = \left(y^2 - x^2\right)$.

12. **B** The shaded area is a right-angled isosceles triangle with height 1. The altitude divides it into two other right-angled isosceles triangles so the base of the shaded area is 2. Therefore the area is $\frac{1}{2} \times 2 \times 1 = 1$.

13. D   Let the length of the first race be d and Rosie's average speed in this race be v (in appropriate units). Thus her time in this race was $\frac{d}{v}$.

The length of the second race was $d \times \frac{6}{5}$ and her average speed was $v \times \frac{4}{5}$. Hence her time for the second race was

$\left(d \times \frac{6}{5}\right) \div \left(v \times \frac{4}{5}\right) = \frac{6}{5} \times \frac{5}{4} \times \frac{d}{v} = \frac{3}{2} \times \frac{d}{v}$. She took 50% longer.

14. A   The altitude of an equilateral triangle of side 1 is $\frac{1}{2}\sqrt{3}$.

Hence $XY = 2 \times \frac{1}{2}\sqrt{3} - 1 = \sqrt{3} - 1$.

15. A $5^8 \times 8^5 = 5^8 \times 2^{15} = (5 \times 2)^8 \times 2^7 = 128 \times 100\,000\,000 = 12\,800\,000\,000$ which has 11 digits.

16. B   Let the radius of the base of the top part of the cone (painted red) be r. So, by similarity, the radius of the red and white cone must be $4r$ and the radius of the whole cone must be $6r$. In the same way, the slant heights are l, $4l$ and $6l$. From the formula $\pi r l$ for the curved surface area of a cone, it follows that the areas are $\pi r l$, $\pi \times 4r \times 4l$ and $\pi \times 6r \times 6l$. Thus the white area is $16\pi r l - \pi r l = 15\pi r l$ and the red area is $36\pi r l - 15\pi r l = 21\pi r l$ giving the ratio white area : red area $= 15\pi r l : 21\pi r l = 5 : 7$.

17. C   Consider a group of 100 children, 10 from Scotland and 90 from elsewhere. Then using x to represent the required average we have

$90x + 10 \times 5.35 = 100 \times 3.10$. Hence $90x = 310 - 53.5 = 256.5$ giving $x = 2.85$.

18. E   The line $y = x - 4$ is closest to the origin at the point $(2, -2)$, a distance of $\sqrt{8} = 2\sqrt{2}$.

All the points on the circle $x^2 + y^2 = 4$ are 2 units from the origin.

The hyperbola $y = \frac{4}{x}$ is closest to the origin at its two nodes $(2, 2)$ and $(-2, -2)$, a distance of $\sqrt{8} = 2\sqrt{2}$.

The parabola $y = x^2 + 4$ has a local minimum at $(0, 4)$ so no point on it is closer than 4 units.

The curve $y = x^4 - 4$ cuts the x-axis at $\left(-\sqrt{2}, 0\right)$ and $\left(\sqrt{2}, 0\right)$, both of which are closer to the origin than any of the points on the other four alternatives.

19. C $2002 = 2 \times 1001 = 2 \times 7 \times 11 \times 13$ which is the product of four primes.

Since $2003 < 13 \times 13 \times 13$, for 2003 to be a product of three distinct primes, at least one of them must be less than 13. However, none of 2, 3, 5, 7 or 11 is a factor of 2003.

$2004 = 2 \times 2 \times 3 \times 167$ which has a repeated prime factor.

$2005 = 5 \times 401$ which is the product of two primes.

$2006 = 2 \times 1003 = 2 \times 17 \times 59$ and is therefore the next year which is the product of three distinct primes.

20. C Let the points of contacts of the tangents be P, Q and R as shown and let $\angle XOQ = x$ and $\angle QOY = y$. Then since OX is the axis of symmetry of the tangent kite $OPXQ$, it bisects $\angle POQ$ so $\angle XOP = x$. Similarly $\angle ROY = y$. Thus, in the quadrilateral $OPBR$ we have

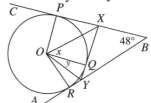

$$2x + 2y + 2 \times 90° + 48° = 360°$$

i.e. $$2(x + y) = 132°$$

i.e. $$x + y = 66°$$

21. C Let the letters be p, q, r, s, t and the corresponding houses be P, Q, R, S, T. The number of ways of correctly putting in two letters is $\frac{5!}{2!3!} = 10$. For the third letter, there are just two wrong choices and then the others are fixed. (If p, q have been correctly delivered, then clearly r can go to S or T. If r is put to S then t must go to R and s to T. If r is put to T then t must go to S and s to R.)

So there are just $2 \times 10 = 20$ ways.

22. E $4^{\left(\frac{n-1}{n+1}\right)}$ is an integer if the value of $\frac{n-1}{n+1}$ is $0, \frac{1}{2}, 1, \frac{3}{2}, \ldots$ i.e. $\frac{n-1}{n+1} = \frac{k}{2}$ where $k = 0, 1, 2, 3, \ldots$

Let $\frac{k}{2} = \frac{n-1}{n+1} = \frac{n+1-2}{n+1} = 1 - \frac{2}{n+1}$. Then $k = 2 - \frac{4}{n+1}$. For k to be an integer, the only possible values of $n + 1$ are $-4, -2, -1, 1, 2, 4$; i.e. the possible values of n are $-5, -3, -2, 0, 1, 3$.

The corresponding values of k are $3, 4, 6, -2, 0, 1$. However, k cannot be negative and therefore $n = 0$ is not valid.

Therefore the five possible values of n are $-5, -3, -2, 1, 3$.

23. A Draw in the lines and attach labels as shown and let the circle have radius r. (O is the centre of the circle.) In $\triangle OPB$: $OP = OB \sin 30° = \frac{1}{2}r$. Then, looking at $\triangle OPQ$, $\angle OPQ = 150°$ so we can apply the Cosine Rule to obtain PQ.

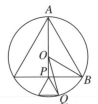

$$OQ^2 = PQ^2 + OP^2 - 2PQ.OP \cos 150°$$

Writing $PQ = ry$, this gives

$$r^2 = r^2 y^2 + \tfrac{1}{4}r^2 - 2 \times ry \times \tfrac{1}{2}r \left(-\tfrac{\sqrt{3}}{2}\right)$$

i.e. $$1 = y^2 + \tfrac{1}{4} + \tfrac{1}{2}\sqrt{3}y$$

$$\left(y + \tfrac{1}{4}\sqrt{3}\right)^2 = \tfrac{3}{4} + \left(\tfrac{\sqrt{3}}{4}\right)^2 = \tfrac{15}{16}$$

$$\therefore \quad y = \tfrac{\sqrt{15}}{4} - \tfrac{\sqrt{3}}{4} \qquad \text{(ignoring the negative root)}.$$

Hence the ratio

$$\frac{AB}{PQ} = \frac{\sqrt{3}r}{\left(\frac{\sqrt{15}-\sqrt{3}}{4}\right)r} = \frac{4}{(\sqrt{5}-1)} \times \frac{\sqrt{5}+1}{\sqrt{5}+1} = \sqrt{5}+1.$$

24. E   The possible combinations of Knaves who ate the tarts are shown in the table below. A tick opposite the letter of the statement means that the statement is consistent with that combination having eaten the tarts

	None	C	D	S	CD	DS	CS	CDS
A	✓	✗	✗	✗	✗	✗	✗	✗
B	✗	✓	✗	✗	✓	✗	✓	✓
C	✗	✓	✓	✓	✗	✗	✗	✗
D	✓	✓	✓	✓	✓	✗	✓	✗
E	✗	✗	✗	✗	✓	✓	✓	✓

The only column which contains exactly one tick is 'DS' in row E. Therefore E is the correct statement.

25. D   Let the original triangle be ABC and use a, b, c for the opposite sides as normal. Then the sides of the three inner squares are a, b and c. Hence $A_1 = a^2 + b^2 + c^2$.

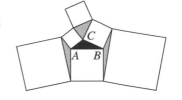

We now move towards the three outer squares but first apply the Cosine Rule to the original triangle in three ways.

$$a^2 = b^2 + c^2 - 2bc\cos A \Rightarrow 2bc\cos A = b^2 + c^2 - a^2 \quad (1)$$

$$b^2 = a^2 + c^2 - 2ac\cos B \Rightarrow 2ac\cos B = a^2 + c^2 - b^2 \quad (2)$$

$$c^2 = a^2 + b^2 - 2ab\cos C \Rightarrow 2ab\cos C = a^2 + b^2 - c^2 \quad (3)$$

From (1), the area of the lower left square is given by

$$b^2 + c^2 - 2bc\cos(180° - A) = b^2 + c^2 + 2bc\cos A = 2(b^2 + c^2) - a^2.$$

From (2), the area of the lower right square is given by

$$a^2 + c^2 - 2ac\cos(180° - B) = a^2 + c^2 + 2ac\cos B = 2(a^2 + c^2) - b^2.$$

From (3), the area of the top square is given by

$$a^2 + b^2 - 2ab\cos(180° - C) = a^2 + b^2 + 2ab\cos C = 2(a^2 + b^2) - c^2.$$

Thus $A_2 = 4(a^2 + b^2 + c^2) - (a^2 + b^2 + c^2) = 3A_1.$

SMC solutions 2002

*A B C C E * C B D A E * A A D E D * E D B C A * D B E B C*

1.   **A**   A square of area 4 cm^2 has side 2 cm and therefore its perimeter is 8 cm. A square of area 1 cm^2 has side 1 cm, so its perimeter is 4 cm.

2.   **B**   The lines which make up a network are known as 'edges' and edges meet at points called 'nodes'. The *order* of a node is the number of edges which meet at that node. So network *A* has three nodes of order 2 and two of order 3. For a network to be traversable the number of odd-ordered nodes must be either 0 or 2. If there are no odd-ordered nodes, it is possible to trace out the network starting at any node. If there are two odd-ordered nodes, these must be the start and finish of the path which traces out the network. Network *B* has four odd-ordered nodes and therefore is not traversable.

(Is it possible for a network to have exactly one odd-ordered node?)

3.   **C**   The points which Peri reaches from the second day onwards are (2, 3), (3, 5), (5, 8), (8, 13) and (13, 21) respectively.

4.   **C**   The sum of the digits of both numbers is 45, so both are multiples of 3. Also, both numbers are odd so their product is an odd multiple of 3. Hence there is a remainder of 3 when the product is divided by 6.

5.   **E** $2002 = 2 \times 7 \times 11 \times 13$; $2^2 + 7^2 + 11^2 + 13^2 = 343$.

6.   **C**   The number of children in the village must be a multiple of both 3 and 7, i.e. it must be a multiple of 21. The only multiple of 21 which is less than 40 is 21 itself and so there are 21 children in the village. Of these, 7 can swim, 14 can ride a bicycle and 3 can do both. The number of children, therefore, who can do at least one of these activities is $7 + 14 - 3 = 18$. So 3 children can neither swim nor ride a bicycle.

7.   **B**   The only two-digit cubes are 27 and 64. If 1 across is 64, then 1 down must also be 64 (the only square between 61 and 69 inclusive), but there must be a different digit in each square so this is impossible. Hence 1 across is 27 and 1 down is 25. The possibilities for 2 down are now 71, 73 and 79 giving 51, 53 and 59 as possibilities for 3 across. Of these, only $53 = 2^2 + 7^2$ can be written as the sum of two squares, so 2 down is 73 and 3 across 53.

8.   **D**   The number of inches in a furlong is 220×36. The number of barleycorns in a furlong is $10 \times 44 \times 54$. So the number of barleycorns in one inch is $\dfrac{10 \times 44 \times 54}{220 \times 36}$, which evaluates to give 3.

9.   **A**   If the trees are planted twice as far apart then the number of trees per hectare will be a quarter of its previous value.

10. E It is not difficult to show that the piece of paper can be folded to create polygons with 6 or 7 or 8 sides. The diagram shows that it *is* also possible to create a 9-sided polygon. When the piece of paper is folded, the fold makes up one side of the resulting polygon. In addition, each of the four corners can contribute a maximum of two sides, so the maximum possible number of sides is $1 + 2 \times 4 = 9$.

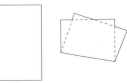

11. A The shaded area $= \frac{2}{3}\pi r^2 + \frac{1}{3}(4\pi r^2 - \pi r^2) = \frac{5}{3}\pi r^2$.
The unshaded area $= 4\pi r^2 - \frac{5}{3}\pi r^2 = \frac{7}{3}\pi r^2$. Hence the required ratio is $5 : 7$.

12. A Let yesterday's prices of a goose and an elephant be x and $99x$ respectively. Today, these prices are $\dfrac{11x}{10}$ and $\dfrac{9}{10} \times 99x$ respectively, so the required number is $\dfrac{9}{10} \times 99x \div \dfrac{11x}{10} = 81$.

13. D The number of different arrangements of the four cards which are dealt is $4 \times 3 \times 2 \times 1 = 24$. In only one of these will the four cards be in descending order.

14. E In returning to its original position, the centre of the disc moves around the circumference of a circle of diameter $2d$, i.e. a distance $2\pi d$. As the disc does not slip, its centre moves a distance πd when the disc makes one complete turn about its centre, so two complete turns are made.

15. D For the equation to have integer solutions, it must be possible to write $x^2 + nx - 16$ in the form $(x - \alpha)(x - \beta)$, where α and β are integers. Therefore $x^2 + nx - 16 = x^2 - (\alpha + \beta)x + \alpha\beta$ and we require that $\alpha\beta = -16$. The possible integer values of α, β are $1, -16$; $-1, 16$; $2, -8$; $-2, 8$; $4, -4$ (we do not count $-16, 1$ as being distinct from $1, -16$, for instance). As $n = -(\alpha + \beta)$, the possible values of n are $15, -15, 6, -6$ and 0.

16. E The triangle whose vertices are the centres of the three circles has sides of length $\sqrt{2}$, $\sqrt{2}$ and 2 and is, therefore, a right-angled isosceles triangle. The perimeter of the shaded region is

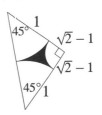

$$2 \times \frac{1}{8} \times 2\pi + \frac{1}{4} \times 2\pi(\sqrt{2} - 1) = \frac{\pi\sqrt{2}}{2} = \frac{\pi}{\sqrt{2}}.$$

17. D Puzzle number 351 is in volume 5, so there is a maximum of 87 puzzles per volume (since, if there were 88, then puzzle 351 would be in volume 4). Also, puzzle number 689 is in volume 8, so there are at least 87 puzzles per volume (since, if there were 86, then puzzle 689 would be in volume 9).

18. B Note that $81 = 3^4$. Therefore $\dfrac{81^{20}}{3^{81}} = \dfrac{3^{80}}{3^{81}} = \dfrac{1}{3}$.

19. C   Let the point on the ground vertically below T be T', let O be the point where line DB meets the wall and let $OT' = x$.

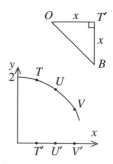

Then, since $\angle T'OB = \angle T'BO = 45°$, $T'B = x$.

As $TB = 2$, $TT' = \sqrt{4 - x^2}$.

Hence, with respect to axes shown in the diagram, the equation of the curve on which T, U, V, ... lie is

$$y = \sqrt{4 - x^2}, \text{ i.e. } x^2 + y^2 = 4, x \geqslant 0, y \geqslant 0$$

which is the equation of part of a circle of radius 2.

20. A   We note that the graph of $y = \sin(x^2)$ passes through the origin and also is symmetrical about the y-axis, since $(-x)^2 = x^2$. For $-\sqrt{\pi} \leqslant x \leqslant \sqrt{\pi}$, $\sin(x^2) \geqslant 0$ and the only one of the graphs to satisfy all of these conditions is A.

[Note that the graph of $y = \sin(x^2)$ has range $-1 \leqslant y \leqslant 1$ and crosses the x-axis when $x = \pm\sqrt{n\pi}$ for all natural numbers n.]

21. D   Note that, as on the question paper, $a° = 20°, b° = 30°, c° = 40°$.

$\angle UPT = \angle PTQ + \angle PQT$ (exterior angle of $\triangle PQT$)

      $= 50°$.

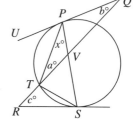

$\angle TSP = \angle UPT$ (alternate segment theorem)

      $= 50°$.

$\angle RST = \angle TPS = x°$ (alternate segment theorem).

$\angle STV = \angle TRS + \angle TSR$ (exterior angle of $\triangle RST$)

      $= (40 + x)°$.

So $\angle STP = (60 + x)°$. Then in $\triangle STP$: $(60 + x) + x + 50 = 180$ (angle sum of a triangle).

Hence $x = 35$.

22. B $y = \dfrac{x}{x + \dfrac{x}{x+y}} = \dfrac{x(x+y)}{x(x+y) + x}$ $(x \neq 0, x+y \neq 0, x+y+1 \neq 0)$

                $= \dfrac{x+y}{x+y+1}$

i.e. $y(x + y + 1) = x + y$

i.e. $y^2 + xy - x = 0$.

For y to be real, this quadratic equation must have real roots so $x^2 + 4x \geqslant 0$, i.e. $x(x + 4) \geqslant 0$.

This condition is satisfied when $x \leqslant -4$ or when $x \geqslant 0$.

However, $x \neq 0$ so y is real when $x \leqslant -4$ or when $x > 0$.

23. E   As $\angle XAB = 90°$ (interior angle of a square) and $\angle XAY = 90°$ (angle in a semi-circle), ABY is a straight line.

The length of the diagonal of square $XABD = \sqrt{2}$ and the length of the diagonal of square $YCBE = AY - AB$ i.e. $\sqrt{3} - 1$.

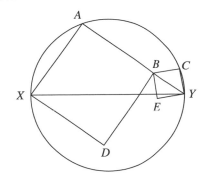

Hence the required ratio is

$$\left(\sqrt{2}\right)^2 : \left(\sqrt{3} - 1\right)^2 = 2 : \left(4 - 2\sqrt{3}\right)$$
$$= 1 : \left(2 - \sqrt{3}\right).$$

(The diagram shows C on the circumference of the circle. It is left as an exercise for the reader to prove that this is the case.)

24. B

$$f(2008) = \frac{f(2005) - 1}{f(2005) + 1} = \frac{\dfrac{f(2002) - 1}{f(2002) + 1} - 1}{\dfrac{f(2002) - 1}{f(2002) + 1} + 1} = \frac{f(2002) - 1 - (f(2002) + 1)}{f(2002) - 1 + f(2002) + 1}$$

$$= \frac{-2}{2 \times f(2002)} = \frac{-1}{f(2002)}$$

Hence $f(2002) \times f(2008) = -1$ provided that $f(2002) \neq 0$.

25. C   Let N have x digits, so that $x \leqslant 2002$.

When the digit 1 is placed at its end, N becomes $10N + 1$.

When 1 is placed in front of it, N becomes $10^x + N$.

Therefore: $10N + 1 = 3\left(10^x + N\right)$, i.e. $7N = 3 \times 10^x - 1$.

So we need to find which of the numbers 2, 29, 299, 2999, 29999, ... are divisible by 7.

The first such number is 299999 (corresponding to $x = 5$), giving $N = 42857$ and we check that $428571 = 3 \times 142857$.

The next such numbers correspond to $x = 11, x = 17, x = 23, x = 29$ and the largest number in the given range corresponds to $x = 1997$.

The number of different values of N, therefore, is $1 + (1997 - 5) \div 6 = 333$.

SMC solutions 2003

*D A A C A * B C E B D * C C A E D * A C E E B * B C B A D*

1. **D** The differences between the given years and 2003 are 498, 398, 298, 198 and 98 respectively. Of these, only 198 is a multiple of 11.

2. **A** The area of a triangle $= \frac{1}{2}$ base × perpendicular height. The four triangles have bases of equal length, since $QR = RS = ST = TU$, and the same perpendicular height, PU.

3. **A** $2 \oplus 6 = \sqrt{12 + 4} = 4$, so $(2 \oplus 6) \oplus 8 = 4 \oplus 8 = \sqrt{32 + 4} = 6$.

4. **C** Sophie, Stephanie and Sarah are all shorter than Susan. However, Susan is shorter than Sandra, so Sandra is the tallest of the five girls.

5. **A** Second prize was $18 \times £4.25 - 18 \times 25p = 18 \times £4 = £72$. So in 2000, second prize was £22 more than first prize!

6. **B** Point F must be reached directly from B, C or E. There is one route from A to B, one route from A to C, and there are three routes from A to E. So the number of possible routes is $1 + 1 + 3 = 5$.

7. **C** For ropes of the same material and same length, the weight is directly proportional to the cross-sectional area and hence to the square of the diameter of the rope. So the weight, in kg, of the second rope
$$\approx 2.7 \times \frac{11^2}{9^2} = 2.7 \times \frac{121}{81} = \frac{121}{30} \approx 4.$$

8. **E** Let the smaller number be x and the larger number y.
Then $y - x = \frac{1}{4}(y + x)$; $4y - 4x = y + x$; $3y = 5x$; hence $x : y = 3 : 5$.

9. **B** Mary and Margaret's salaries before the pay rises were $£23\,100 \times \frac{100}{110}$ and $£23\,100 \times \frac{100}{105}$ respectively, i.e. £21 000 and £22 000 respectively. So the difference was £1000.

10. **D** The average speed of the balloon, in km/h, $\approx \dfrac{\pi \times 12750}{13\frac{1}{2} \times 24} \approx \dfrac{\pi \times 1000}{24}$
$\approx \pi \times 40 \approx 120$.

11. **C** When Zerk made a beeline back to the hive, the distance she travelled is equal to the length of a space diagonal of a cube of side 1m, i.e.
$\sqrt{1^2 + 1^2 + 1^2}$ m $= \sqrt{3}$ m.
So the total distance she flew $= (3 + \sqrt{3})$m.

12. C   Using similar triangles: $\dfrac{b}{3} = \dfrac{a}{7} = \dfrac{5}{10}$ so $a = 3\frac{1}{2}$ and $b = 1\frac{1}{2}$. Hence $a + b = 5$.

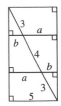

Alternatively, if a copy of the large triangle is rotated through $180°$ about the midpoint of its hypotenuse, then the two triangles form a rectangle and it is clear that $a + b = 5$.

13. A   Since $x^3 - x = x(x^2 - 1) = (x - 1) \times x \times (x + 1)$, $x^3 - x$ is always the product of three consecutive whole numbers when x is a whole number. As one of these must be a multiple of 3, $x^3 - x$ will be divisible by 3. Substituting 2 for x in the expressions in B, C and E and substituting 3 for x in the expression in D results in numbers which are not divisible by 3.

14. E   As shown in the diagram, lines A, B, C and D determine a square of side $\sqrt{2}$.

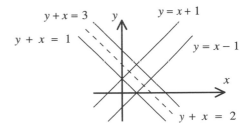

15. D   The only square numbers which are factors of 2003^{2003} have the form 2003^{2n} for a non-negative integer n. But $2n \leqslant 2003$ so $n = 0, 1, \ldots, 1001$.

16. A   Let the costs in pence of a peach, an orange and a melon be x, y, z respectively. We need $x - y$. We are given that $5x + 3y + 2z = 318$ and $4x + 8y + 3z = 449$. Multiplying the first by 3 and the second by 2 and subtracting gives $7x - 7y = 3 \times 318 - 2 \times 449 = 954 - 898 = 56$, so $x - y = 8$.

(*Note that as we have three unknowns, but only two equations, it is impossible to determine unique values of x, y and z. However, as has been shown, in this case it is possible to calculate the difference between the values of x and y.*)

17. C   Let the midpoint of AF be P; as $AEFG$ is a square, this is also the midpoint of EG. Let EG produced meet CD at Q. Now $AF^2 = AE^2 + EF^2 = 4 + 4 = 8$. So $AF = \sqrt{8} = 2\sqrt{2}$ and hence $PF = PE = \sqrt{2}$.

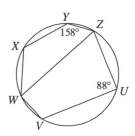

In right-angled triangle CQE:

$$CE^2 = CQ^2 + QE^2 = \left(4 - \sqrt{2}\right)^2 + \left(4 + \sqrt{2}\right)^2$$

$$= 16 - 8\sqrt{2} + 2 + 16 + 8\sqrt{2} + 2 = 36.$$

So the length of CE is 6cm.

18. E $2^{2003} - 2^{2002} - 2^{2001} - 2^{2000} = 2^{2000}\left(2^3 - 2^2 - 2 - 1\right)$
$= 2^{2000}(8 - 4 - 2 - 1) = 2^{2000}$.

19. E   The graph shows that the equation linking y and x is of the form $\dfrac{1}{y} = m\sqrt{x} + c$, where m and c are positive constants. Hence: $y = \dfrac{1}{m\sqrt{x} + c}$

so $y^2 = \dfrac{1}{m^2x + 2mc\sqrt{x} + c^2}$.

Of the given equations, only E is of the correct form. It is obtained from the equation above when $m = c = 1$.

20. B   The opposite angles of a cyclic quadrilateral add up to $180°$ so $\angle XWZ = 180° - 158° = 22°$; $\angle VWZ = 180° - 88° = 92°$; hence $\angle VWX = 92° + 22° = 114°$.

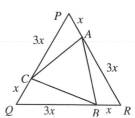

21. B   Triangles BCQ, CAP and ABR are congruent since each has sides of x and $3x$ and an included angle of $60°$ (SAS).

Consider triangle BCQ: its base, BQ, and height are $\frac{3}{4}$ and $\frac{1}{4}$ respectively of the base, QR, and height of triangle PQR.

So area of triangle $BCQ = \frac{3}{16} \times$ area of triangle PQR and the area of triangle $ABC = (1 - 3 \times \frac{3}{16}) \times$ area of triangle $PQR = \frac{7}{16} \times 1 = \frac{7}{16}$.

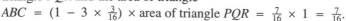

22. C   To count the number of ways, it is necessary to have a structure. One strategy is to consider the number of £2 coins and then £1 coins; the balance can be made up with 50p coins.

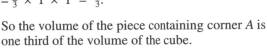

Number of £2 coins	50	49	48	...	0
Maximum number of £1 coins	0	2	4	...	100
Ways	1	3	5	...	101

Total ways $= 1 + 3 + 5 + \ldots + 101 = \frac{1}{2} \times 51(1 + 101) = 51 \times 51 = 2601$.

23. B   The piece containing corner A is a pyramid. Its base is the square $ADTX$ and its vertex is B. Let the length of the side of the cube be 1 unit: then the volume of the pyramid $= \frac{1}{3}$ base area $\times$ height $= \frac{1}{3} \times 1 \times 1 = \frac{1}{3}$.

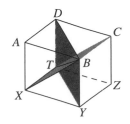

So the volume of the piece containing corner A is one third of the volume of the cube.

24. A   Tangents to a circle from an exterior point are equal in length so $BT = BY = \frac{1}{2}BA = \frac{1}{2}\sqrt{2}$.
Radius $R = OT = OB - BT = 1 - \frac{1}{2}\sqrt{2}$.
Triangle OBY is isosceles with
$OY = BY = \frac{1}{2}\sqrt{2}$.
Radius $OZ = OY + YZ = 1$ so
$\frac{1}{2}\sqrt{2} + 2r = 1$ and hence
$r = \frac{1}{2}\left(1 - \frac{1}{2}\sqrt{2}\right) = \frac{1}{2}R$.

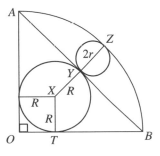

25. D

$$\frac{1}{x} + \frac{2}{y} = \frac{3}{19}.$$

i.e. $38x + 19y = 3xy$.

i.e. $9xy - 114x - 57y + 38 \times 19 = 38 \times 19$.

i.e. $(3x - 19)(3y - 38) = 2 \times 19^2$.

The factors of 2×19^2 are $1, 2, 19, 38, 361$ and 722 and $3x - 19$ has to be one of these.

If $3x - 19 = 1, 19$ or 361, then x is not an integer. If $3x - 19 = 2$, then $x = 7$ and $3y - 38 = 361$ giving $y = 133$. If $3x - 19 = 38$, then $x = 19$ and $3y - 38 = 19$ giving $y = 19$ as well. If $3x - 19 = 722$, then $x = 247$ and $3y - 38 = 1$ giving $y = 13$.

(The equation $\dfrac{1}{x} + \dfrac{2}{y} = \dfrac{3}{p}$ always has exactly 3 solutions when x and y are positive integers and p is a prime greater than or equal to 5. Can you prove this result?)

SMC solutions 2004

*D E D D B * E C C D B * A C A C C * E A A B E * B B D E C*

1.   **D**   For the largest of the numbers to be as large as possible, the other two numbers must be as small as possible, that is 1 and 2.

2.   **E**   One million minus one thousand $= 1\,000\,000 - 1000 = 999\,000$. So one million million minus one thousand million $= 999\,000$ million $= 999\,000\,000\,000$.

3.   **D**   Let the fraction of her lolly that Milly has eaten be x. Then Molly has eaten $\frac{1}{2}x$ of her lolly. This means that the fractions they have left are $(1 - x)$ and $(1 - \frac{1}{2}x)$ respectively.
So $1 - \frac{1}{2}x = 3(1 - x)$, that is $5x = 4$, giving $x = \frac{4}{5}$.

4.   **D**   Simon needs to buy as many batches of 5 pies as possible. He buys 400 batches of 5, giving him 2000 pies at a cost of £16. The other 4 pies cost 1p each, making a total of £16.04.

5.   **B**   Let the weights of squares, triangles and circles be s, t, c respectively. Then $c + 3t = 6s$; and $4c + 2t = 8s$, so $2c + t = 4s$. Hence $(c + 3t) + (2c + t) = 10s$.

6.   **E**   From the information given, we can conclude only that Pat is either 23 or 29.

7.   **C**   The original height of 29 feet 3 inches is 351 inches. So after the first bounce the ball reaches a height of 234 inches; after the second bounce the height reached is 156 inches and after the third bounce it reaches a height of 104 inches, i.e. 8 feet 8 inches.

8.   **C** $\angle ACB + \angle ACE + \angle DCE = 180°$
             (angles on a straight line).
So $\angle ACB = 90° - \angle DCE$.
Also, $\angle CDE + \angle CED + \angle DCE = 180°$
             (angle sum of a triangle).

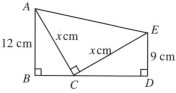

So $\angle CED = 90° - \angle DCE$.
Therefore $\angle ACB = \angle CED$ and we can deduce that triangles ABC and CDE are congruent since they have two pairs of equal angles and one pair of equal sides ($AC = CE$). So BC has length 9 cm and we use Pythagoras' Theorem to see that $x^2 = 12^2 + 9^2 = 225$. Hence $x = 15$.

9.   **D**   There are eight 2-digit numbers which satisfy the required condition (12, 23, ... , 89), seven 3-digit numbers (123, 234, ... , 789), six 4-digit numbers (1234, 2345, ... , 6789) and one 5-digit number (12345).

10.   **B**   Let the small circles have radius r. Then the large circle has radius $3r$. The unshaded area is $7\pi r^2$, while the shaded area is $\pi(3r)^2 - 7\pi r^2 = 2\pi r^2$. So the required ratio is 7:2.

11.   **A**   In one hour the fraction of lawn which has been mowed is $\frac{1}{3} + \frac{1}{4} + \frac{1}{6} = \frac{3}{4}$. So the time taken to mow the lawn is $\frac{4}{3}$ hours, that is 1 hour 20 minutes.

12. C The hexagonal face has 6 vertices and each of these must be connected to at least one other vertex in a different plane from that of the hexagonal face. So this requires at least 6 edges. Also the hexagonal face itself contributes 6 edges to the polyhedron so the polyhedron has a minimum of 12 edges. We now need to consider if such a polyhedron with 12 edges exists. It does, in the form of a pyramid on a hexagonal base, so the smallest number of edges the polyhedron could have is indeed 12.

13. A The last digit of 3^4 is 1, as is the last digit of 7^4 and the last digit of 9^2. So the last digit of $(3^4)^{501}$, that is of 3^{2004}, is 1. Similarly, the last digit of $(7^4)^{501}$, that is of 7^{2004}, is 1 and the last digit of $(9^2)^{1002}$, that is of 9^{2004}, is 1. Furthermore, $1^{2004} = 1$ and the last digit of 5^{2004} is 5. So the units digit of the expression is $1 + 1 + 5 + 1 + 1$, that is 9.

14. C Let the side of the cube be of length 2. Then $LM = MN = \sqrt{1^2 + 1^2} = \sqrt{2}$; $LN = \sqrt{1^2 + 1^2 + 2^2} = \sqrt{6}$. So LMN is an isosceles triangle with sides $\sqrt{2}, \sqrt{2}, \sqrt{6}$. Thus $\cos\angle NLM = \dfrac{\sqrt{6}/2}{\sqrt{2}} = \dfrac{\sqrt{3}}{2}$; hence $\angle NLM = 30° = \angle MNL$. So $\angle LMN = 120°$.
(Alternatively, it may be shown that L, M and N, together with the midpoints of three other edges of the cube, are the vertices of a regular hexagon. So $\angle LMN$ may be shown to be 120°.)

15. C The core of the trunk occupies 81% of the volume of the trunk. Assuming that the trunk is cylindrical, this means that 81% of the cross-sectional area of the trunk is occupied by the core. Now $\sqrt{0.81} = 0.9$, so the diameter of the core is 90% of the diameter of the trunk, that is 36 cm. Hence the thickness of the bark is 4 cm $\div 2$, that is 2 cm.

16. E Let the radius of the arc with centre R be r cm. Then $QT = (17 - r)$ cm and $PU = (15 - r)$ cm. Now $QS = QT$ (radii of arc ST) and $PS = PU$ (radii of arc SU), so $QP = (17 - r + 15 - r)\,\text{cm} = (32 - 2r)\,\text{cm}$. But, by Pythagoras' Theorem:

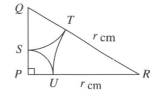

$$QP = \sqrt{17^2 - 15^2}\,\text{cm} = \sqrt{(17+15)(17-15)}\,\text{cm} = 8\,\text{cm}.$$

So $32 - 2r = 8$, that is $r = 12$.

17. A Consider the four portions AB, BO, OC and CD of the graph shown. The graph of $y = f(x)$ contains either portion AB as shown, or the reflection of this portion in the x-axis. The same is true for the other three portions, so the number of different graphs of $y = f(x)$ which would give this graph of $y = |f(x)|$ is $2 \times 2 \times 2 \times 2$ that is 16.

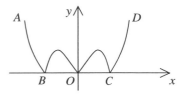

18. A Using the alternate segment theorem: $\angle LMN = \angle PNL = \theta°$.
Also, since $LM = LN$, then $\angle LNM = \angle LMN = \theta°$. So $\angle RNM = (180 - 2\theta)°$
(angles on a straight line).
Now $\angle LMN = \angle RNM + \angle LRP$ (exterior angle theorem), so
$\angle LRP = \angle LMN - \angle RNM = \theta° - (180 - 2\theta)° = (3\theta - 180)°$.

19. B Multiplying the equation $S + M \times C = 64$ by S gives
$S^2 + S \times M \times C = 64S$. Therefore $S^2 + 240 = 64S$, that is
$(S - 60)(S - 4) = 0$. So $S = 60$ or $S = 4$. Multiplying the equation
$S \times C + M = 46$ by M gives $M \times S \times C + M^2 = 46M$. Therefore
$240 + M^2 = 46M$, that is $(M - 40)(M - 6) = 0$. So $M = 40$ or
$M = 6$. If $M = 40$ then $S \times C = 6$, so $C = 6/60$ or $6/4$, neither of
which is a whole number. If $M = 6$ then $S \times C = 40$, so $C = 40/60$ or
$40/4$. Hence the only whole number solutions of the equations are $S = 4$,
$M = 6, C = 10$.

20. E Expressed as the product of prime factors, $396 = 2^2 \times 3^2 \times 11$. Therefore
the lowest positive integer by which it must be multiplied to make a perfect
cube is $2 \times 3 \times 11^2$, that is 726.

21. B Note, from the information given, that $\angle PRQ = \angle RPQ = 45°$; $\angle RQS = 60°$;
$\angle PQS = 30°$.
Applying the Sine Rule to $\triangle SRQ$: $\dfrac{RS}{\sin 60°} = \dfrac{SQ}{\sin 45°}$ and to $\triangle SPQ$:
$\dfrac{SP}{\sin 30°} = \dfrac{SQ}{\sin 45°}$.
Hence $\dfrac{RS}{\sin 60°} = \dfrac{SP}{\sin 30°}$, so $RS : SP = \sin 60° : \sin 30° = \sqrt{3} : 1$.

22. B Let the vertices of the trapezium be
A, B, C, D and let AC meet BD at E,
as shown. Triangles ABE and CDE are
similar since $\angle ABE = \angle CDE$ (alternate
angles) and $\angle AEB = \angle CED$ (vertically
opposite angles). So

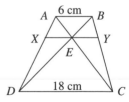

$$\frac{CE}{AE} = \frac{CD}{AB} = \frac{18}{6} = 3.$$

Hence $AC = 4AE$ and, by a similar argument, $BD = 4BE$.
Triangles AXE and ADC are similar since $\angle XAE$ is the same angle as $\angle DAC$
and $\angle AXE = \angle ADC$ (corresponding angles). So $\dfrac{XE}{DC} = \dfrac{AE}{AC} = \dfrac{1}{4}$; hence
$XE = 4.5$ cm.
Applying a similar argument to triangles BYE and BCD, we find that
$YE = 4.5$ cm also. So the length XY is 9 cm.

23. D   First note that 1, 11, 111, 1111, 11111 are not divisible by 7 but that
111111 = 15873 × 7. So any number in which all the digits are the same is
divisible by 7 if the number of digits is a multiple of 6. Therefore the 2004-
digit number 888...888 is a multiple of 7. Similarly, the 2004-digit number
222...222 is a multiple of 7, as is the 2004-digit number 222...229 since it
differs from 222...222 by 7. Furthermore, the 2004-digit number 222...22n
is not a multiple of 7 if n is any digit other than 2 or 9.

Now $N = 222...22n \times 10^{2004} + 888...888$, so if N is divisible by 7 then
222...22n is divisible by 7 and we deduce that $n = 2$ or 9.

24. E   Let A be the centre of one of the
large circles, B the point where the
two large circles touch, C the
centre of the small circle and D the
centre of the largest circle which
can be placed in the shaded region,
i.e. the circle which touches all
three of the given circles. Let the
radius of this circle be r.

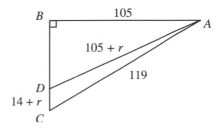

Then $AB = 105; AD = 105 + r, AC = 105 + 14 = 119, CD = 14 + r$.

Applying Pythagoras' Theorem to triangle ABC we find that $BC = \sqrt{119^2 - 105^2}$
$= \sqrt{224 \times 14} = 56$. So $BD = 42 - r$.

Similarly, $(105 + r)^2 = 105^2 + (42 - r)^2$. This leads to the equation
$294r = 42^2$, that is $r = 6$.

25. C
$$\sqrt{x + \tfrac{1}{2}\sqrt{y}} - \sqrt{x - \tfrac{1}{2}\sqrt{y}} = 1.$$

Therefore $x + \tfrac{1}{2}\sqrt{y} - 2\sqrt{x^2 - \tfrac{1}{4}y} + x - \tfrac{1}{2}\sqrt{y} = 1$,

that is $2x - 1 = 2\sqrt{x^2 - \tfrac{1}{4}y}$.

Therefore $4x^2 - 4x + 1 = 4\left(x^2 - \tfrac{1}{4}y\right)$,

that is $y = 4x - 1$.

So y must be 1 less than a multiple of 4.

Of the values offered, the only possibility is 7. This gives $x = 2$, but it is
necessary to check that these values are solutions of the original equation
since they were derived from an argument which involved squaring
equations. It is not difficult to show that $x = 2, y = 7$ satisfy the second
equation in the above solution. We now need to confirm that

$\sqrt{2 + \tfrac{1}{2}\sqrt{7}} - \sqrt{2 - \tfrac{1}{2}\sqrt{7}}$ does indeed equal 1 rather than −1, which we are

able to do since it is clear that $\sqrt{2 + \tfrac{1}{2}\sqrt{7}}$ is greater than $\sqrt{2 - \tfrac{1}{2}\sqrt{7}}$.

SMC solutions 2005

$C\,B\,D\,A\,E * B\,E\,D\,C\,B * A\,D\,D\,C\,E * B\,E\,A\,A\,C * E\,C\,B\,D\,A$

1. C   2005 plus 2005 thousandths = 2005 + 2.005 = 2007.005.

2. B   Let the five consecutive positive integers be $x - 2, x - 1, x, x + 1, x + 2$. Their sum is $5x$, so $5x = 2005$, that is $x = 401$. The five numbers are 399, 400, 401, 402, 403.

3. D   The numbers are 1, 16, 27, 16 and 5 respectively. Their sum is 65, so their mean is 13.

4. A   The smaller square has one ninth of the area of the larger square. So the fraction of the larger square which is shaded is half of eight ninths, that is four ninths.

5. E   Four lengths of the indoor pool are equivalent to five lengths of the outdoor pool. So Rachel swam four ninths of the 63 days, that is 28 days, in the indoor pool.

6. B   The longest side of any triangle is shorter than the sum of the lengths of the other two sides. This condition means that the only possible triangles having different sides of integral unit length, and having perimeters less than 13 units, have sides of length 2, 3, 4 or 2, 4, 5 or 3, 4, 5.

7. E   The sequences have common differences of 7 and 9 respectively. The lowest common multiple of 7 and 9 is 63, so the next term after 2005 to appear in both sequences is $2005 + 63$, that is 2068.

8. D   The first large sheet of paper will hold pages 1, 2, 19 and 20; the second will hold pages 3, 4, 17 and 18; the third will hold pages 5, 6, 15 and 16.

9. C   The product is $\dfrac{3}{2} \times \dfrac{4}{3} \times \dfrac{5}{4} \times \dfrac{6}{5} \times \ldots \times \dfrac{2005}{2004} \times \dfrac{2006}{2005} = \dfrac{2006}{2} = 1003$.

10. B   Let Sam and Pat have £x and £y respectively.
Then $y + 5 = 5(x - 5)$, that is $y = 5x - 30$. Also, $x + 5 = 5(y - 5)$, that is $x = 5y - 30$. Solving these simultaneous equations gives $x = 7.5$ and $y = 7.5$ so the friends have £15 altogether.
(Note: from the information given, we may deduce that Sam and Pat have the same amount of money and this leads to a shorter method:
$x + 5 = 5(x - 5)$, *that is* $x = 5x - 30$, *that is* $x = 7.5$.)

11. A   The diameter of the largest cylinder is 24cm, so the sum of the areas of the horizontal parts of the sculpture, excluding its base, is that of a circle of diameter 24cm, that is 144π cm^2. The sum of the areas of the vertical parts of the sculpture is

$$\left(2\pi \times 1 \times 2 + 2\pi \times 2 \times 2 + 2\pi \times 3 \times 2 + \ldots + 2\pi \times 12 \times 2\right) \text{cm}^2,$$

that is 312π cm^2. So, excluding the base, the total surface area of the sculpture is 456π cm^2.

12. D   As $\sqrt{x}$ lies between 15 and 16, x lies between 225 and 256. The multiples of 7 in this interval are 231, 238, 245 and 252.

13. D   Let a, b, c, d, e, x and y represent the sizes in degrees of certain angles in the figure, as shown and let the points of intersection of AD with EB and EC be X and Y respectively. Angle EXY is an exterior angle of triangle XBD so $x = b + d$. Similarly, angle EYX is an exterior angle of triangle YAC so $y = a + c$. In triangle EXY, $e + x + y = 180$, so $a + b + c + d + e = 180$.

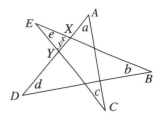

14. C   When divided by 6, a whole number leaves remainder 0, 1, 2, 3, 4 or 5. So the possible remainders when a square number is divided by 6 are the remainders when 0, 1, 4, 9, 16 and 25 are divided by 6. These are 0, 1, 4, 3, 4 and 1 respectively, so a square number cannot leave remainder 2 (or remainder 5) when divided by 6.

15. E   Number the four statements in order from the top. If Alice is the mother, then statements 1 and 4 are both true. If Beth is the mother, then statements 2 and 3 are both true. If Carol is the mother, then all four statements are false. If Diane is the mother, then statements 2 and 4 are both true. However, if Ella is the mother then statements 1, 2 and 3 are false and statement 4 is true, as required.

16. B   Firstly, we note that of the players on the pitch at the end of the game, the goalkeeper is one of two players; the four defenders form one of five different possible combinations, as do the four midfielders, and the two forwards form one of three different possible combinations. So, if up to four substitutes were allowed, the number of different teams which could finish the game would be $2 \times 5 \times 5 \times 3$, that is 150.

From this number we must subtract the number of these teams which require four substitutions to be made. This is $1 \times 4 \times 4 \times 2$, that is 32, so the required number of teams is 118.

17. E   Let A, B, C, D, E be five vertices of the star, as shown. Then $AB = BC = CD = DE = 1$. Each exterior angle of a regular octagon is $360° \div 8$, that is $45°$, so $\angle CBD = \angle CDB = 45°$.

Hence $\angle BCD$ is a right angle and we deduce from the symmetry of the figure that each interior angle of the star is either $90°$ or $225°$. The length of BD is $\sqrt{2}$, so the area of the star is the area of a square of side $2 + \sqrt{2}$ plus the area of four congruent triangles with sides 1, 1, $\sqrt{2}$.

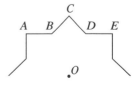

The required area, therefore, is $(2 + \sqrt{2})^2 + 4(\frac{1}{2} \times 1 \times 1)$, that is $6 + 4\sqrt{2} + 2$, that is $8 + 4\sqrt{2}$.

Possible alternative ending: Dissect the star into 8 congruent kites such as $OBCD$. As for a rhombus, the area of a kite is half the product of its diagonals. In this case that is $\frac{1}{2}OC \times BD = \frac{1}{2}(1 + \sqrt{2}) \times \sqrt{2} = \frac{1}{2}(\sqrt{2} + 2)$. Required area is $4(\sqrt{2} + 2)$.

18. A   Let the radii of the two spheres be r_1 and r_2, as shown.
Applying Pythagoras' Theorem: $r_2^2 = r_1^2 + r_1^2 + r_1^2$, so
$r_2 = \sqrt{3}r_1$.
The ratio of the volumes of the spheres
$= r_1^3 : r_2^3 = 1 : (\sqrt{3})^3$, that is $1 : 3\sqrt{3}$.

19. A   When $x \geqslant 0, |x| = x$, so $x|x| = x^2$; when $x < 0, |x| = -x$, so $x|x| = -x^2$.
Only graph A has the same shape as the graph of $y = x^2$ for $x \geqslant 0$ and the
same shape as the graph of $y = -x^2$ for $x < 0$.

20. C   Let the length in metres of the side of a pane be x. Then the
area of one pane $= \frac{1}{2} \times x \times x \times \sin 60° = \frac{\sqrt{3}}{4}x^2$. So

$$\frac{\sqrt{3}}{4}x^2 \approx \frac{6000}{3300}, \text{ that is } x^2 \approx \frac{4 \times 6000}{\sqrt{3} \times 3300}.$$

We conclude that $x^2 \approx \frac{7}{\sqrt{3}} \approx 4$.

21. E   Note that $n^2 - 1$ is divisible by $n - 1$. Thus:

$$\frac{n^2 - 9}{n - 1} = \frac{n^2 - 1}{n - 1} - \frac{8}{n - 1} = n + 1 - \frac{8}{n - 1} \qquad (n \neq 1).$$

So, if n is an integer, then $\dfrac{n^2 - 9}{n - 1}$ is an integer if and only if $n - 1$ divides
exactly into 8.
The possible values of $n - 1$ are $-8, -4, -2, -1, 1, 2, 4, 8$, so n is
$-7, -3, -1, 0, 2, 3, 5, 9$.
The sum of these values is 8.
(*Note that the sum of the 8 values of $n - 1$ is clearly 0, so the sum of the 8
values of n is 8.*)

22. C   There are 81 terms in the series, so, using the formula $S = \frac{1}{2}n(a + l)$ for an
arithmetic series:

$$S = \frac{81}{2}(x + 20 + x + 100) = 81(x + 60).$$

Now 81 is a perfect square, so S is a perfect square if and only if $x + 60$ is a
perfect square. As x is a positive integer, the smallest possible value of x is 4.

23. B   We note from the symmetry of the figure that the three small circles have the same radius. Let this be r and let the radius of the large circle be s. Let A, B, C, D, E be the points shown on the diagram.

By symmetry, $\angle DAE = 30°$.

Now $\frac{DE}{AD} = \sin 30° = \frac{1}{2}$ so AD has length $2s$. Similarly, AB has length $2r$.

Since $AD = AB + BC + CD$, the length of AD is also given by $2r + r + s$. Hence $2s = 3r + s$, i.e. $s = 3r$.

Also, $\dfrac{DE}{AE} = \dfrac{s}{^3/_2} = \tan 30° = \dfrac{1}{\sqrt{3}}$ so $s = \dfrac{3}{2\sqrt{3}}$. Hence $r = \dfrac{1}{2\sqrt{3}}$.

Thus the shaded area $= \pi s^2 + 3\pi r^2 = \pi \times \frac{9}{12} + 3\pi \times \frac{1}{12} = \pi$.

24. D   When $n!$ is written in full, the number of zeros at the end of the number is equal to the power of 5 when $n!$ is written as the product of prime factors, because there is at least that high a power of 2 available. For example, $12! = 1 \times 2 \times 3 \times \ldots \times 12 = 2^{10} \times 3^5 \times 5^2 \times 7 \times 11$.

This may be written as $2^8 \times 3^5 \times 7 \times 11 \times 10^2$, so $12!$ ends in 2 zeros, as $2^8 \times 3^5 \times 7 \times 11$ is not a multiple of 10.

We see that $24!$ ends in 4 zeros as 5, 10, 15 and 20 all contribute one 5 when $24!$ is written as the product of prime factors, but $25!$ ends in 6 zeros because $25 = 5 \times 5$ and hence contributes two 5s. So there is no value of n for which $n!$ ends in 5 zeros.

Similarly, there is no value of n for which $n!$ ends in 11 zeros since $49!$ ends in 10 zeros and $50!$ ends in 12 zeros. The full set of values of k less than 50 for which it is impossible to find a value of n such that $n!$ ends in k zeros is 5, 11, 17, 23, 29, 30 (since $124!$ ends in 28 zeros and $125!$ ends in 31 zeros), 36, 42, 48.

25. A

$$\frac{1}{\sqrt{2005 + \sqrt{2005^2 - 1}}} = \frac{1}{\sqrt{1003 + 1002 + \sqrt{(2005 + 1)(2005 - 1)}}}$$

$$= \frac{1}{\sqrt{(\sqrt{1003})^2 + 2\sqrt{1003}\sqrt{1002} + (\sqrt{1002})^2}}$$

$$= \frac{1}{\sqrt{(\sqrt{1003} + \sqrt{1002})^2}} = \frac{1}{\sqrt{1003} + \sqrt{1002}}$$

$$= \frac{(\sqrt{1003} - \sqrt{1002})}{(\sqrt{1003} - \sqrt{1002})(\sqrt{1003} + \sqrt{1002})}$$

$$= \frac{(\sqrt{1003} - \sqrt{1002})}{1003 - 1002} = \sqrt{1003} - \sqrt{1002}.$$

Section 3

**Answers grids
and
details of UKMT publications**

Junior Mathematical Challenge

Name: . . . .

	Year	Year	Year	Year	Year
Question					
1					
2					
3					
4					
5					
6					
7					
8					
9					
10					
11					
12					
13					
14					
15					
16					
17					
18					
19					
20					
21					
22					
23					
24					
25					

Junior Mathematical Challenge

Name: . . . .

	Year	Year	Year	Year	Year
Question					
1					
2					
3					
4					
5					
6					
7					
8					
9					
10					
11					
12					
13					
14					
15					
16					
17					
18					
19					
20					
21					
22					
23					
24					
25					

Intermediate Mathematical Challenge

Name: . . . .

	Year	Year	Year	Year	Year
Question					
1					
2					
3					
4					
5					
6					
7					
8					
9					
10					
11					
12					
13					
14					
15					
16					
17					
18					
19					
20					
21					
22					
23					
24					
25					

Intermediate Mathematical Challenge

Name: . . . .

	Year	Year	Year	Year	Year
Question					
1					
2					
3					
4					
5					
6					
7					
8					
9					
10					
11					
12					
13					
14					
15					
16					
17					
18					
19					
20					
21					
22					
23					
24					
25					

Senior Mathematical Challenge

Name: . . . .

Question	Year	Year	Year	Year	Year
1					
2					
3					
4					
5					
6					
7					
8					
9					
10					
11					
12					
13					
14					
15					
16					
17					
18					
19					
20					
21					
22					
23					
24					
25					

Senior Mathematical Challenge

Name: . . . .

	Year	Year	Year	Year	Year
Question					
1					
2					
3					
4					
5					
6					
7					
8					
9					
10					
11					
12					
13					
14					
15					
16					
17					
18					
19					
20					
21					
22					
23					
24					
25					

UKMT PUBLICATIONS

Plane Euclidean Geometry: Theory and Problems by CJ Bradley and AD Gardiner

An excellent book for students aged 15-18 and teachers who want to learn how to solve problems in elementary Euclidean geometry. The book follows the development of Euclid; contents include Pythagoras, trigonometry, circle theorems, and Ceva and Menelaus. The book contains hundreds of problems, many with hints and solutions.

Introductions to Number Theory and Inequalities by CJ Bradley

This 294-page book, split in to two distinct sections, provides stimulating material for students aged 15-18. Topics covered in the Number Theory section include prime numbers, Pell's equation, recurring decimals, and modulo arithmetic. The Introduction to Inequalities section contains topics including Arithmetic and Geometric means, geometric inequalities, and the Cauchy-Schwarz inequality.

The book contains full commentary, with complete solutions to all questions.

UKMT Yearbook

The 2005-2006 Yearbook was our eighth Yearbook, having published each year since 1998-1999.

Edited by Bill Richardson, the Yearbook documents all the UKMT activities from that particular year. It includes all the challenge papers and solutions at every level; list of high scorers; tales from the IMO and Olympiad training camps; details of the UKMT's other activities; and a round-up of some overseas mathematical associations.

Past Paper Booklets – Follow-on Rounds

The JMO booklet contains the last four years' papers and solutions for the Junior Mathematical Olympiad, the follow up to the JMC.

The 2006 IMOK booklet contains the papers and solutions for the suite of Intermediate follow-on rounds – the Kangaroo Grey, the Kangaroo Pink, Cayley, Hamilton and Maclaurin. We also have IMOK booklets currently available from 2005, 2004 and 2003.

The two BMO booklets contain material for the British Mathematical Olympiad Round 1. One contains papers and solutions for 2001-2004, and the other for 1997-2000.

Past Paper Booklets – Junior, Intermediate and Senior Challenges.

If you would like further copies of our Challenge past papers, we also sell booklets containing the Mathematics Challenge question papers, solutions, and a summary chart of all the answers.

The Junior and Intermediate booklets contain material for 5 years, and the Senior Challenge booklet for 4 years.

To order any UKMT publications, please visit our website at

www.ukmt.org

or contact the UKMT Maths Challenges Office.